gems
&
jewels

FACT & FABLE

CHRISTOPHER CAVEY

STUDIO EDITIONS

Gems and Jewels: Fact and Fable
published in 1992 by Studio Editions Ltd.
Princess House, 50 Eastcastle Street
London W1N 7AP

Printed and bound in Singapore

ISBN 1 85170 744 1

CONTENTS

Acknowledgements 7

Introduction 9

ACKNOWLEDGEMENTS

This book was written with the intention to provide the reader with an introduction to the complex, wondrous and beautiful world of gems and jewels. It is hoped that it will offer a modest acquaintanceship with this enormous subject. By its very nature, this book cannot cover every aspect of the subject, so it has been designed to concentrate principally on the materials that are relatively accessible to the general public. There are many comprehensive works written on gems and jewels, and the inclusion of a relatively large bibliographical section is designed to assist the reader in further research.

I have to thank many people who have assisted me over the years and, more especially, in the writing of this work. I must primarily express my gratitude to Janet who has had the most difficult of tasks managing our business, whilst I was engaged in writing. She has made an invaluable contribution, both reading

An engraving illustrating one of the Mogul Emperors at his annual weighing, against gems, precious jewels, and metals. Published in 1741. Photograph courtesy of C. Cavey.

through the manuscript and making many helpful suggestions. I must also thank my mother, she too read through the scripts and provided an innocent untarnished view from outside the gemmological world. Her help in the compilation of the bibliographic section is duly acknowledged.

Thanks must go to my good friend Mr Alan Jobbins, for his advice, comments, and editing ability, and his considerable support in allowing a number of his superb photographs to appear in this work; and to my friend Mr Brian S. Lloyd of Gregory Bottley and Lloyd for the use of many colour pictures of rough gem materials. I would like to express my gratitude to Mrs W. Bottley, Mr G. Dreher, and Mr P.V. Keane for the use of their superb colour photographs of gemstone carvings. I must also thank Mr Patrick Aldridge for allowing me to use in this book some colour transparencies of a few of the outstanding gems and jewels that pass through his hands at Gemcut SA in Geneva.

There are many others who have made contributions to this work, and I take this opportunity of acknowledging my debt to them now. I sincerely apologize for not naming them in person, but I hope they will be duly understanding.

Lastly, I must thank the publishers of this work, who have tried hard to understand the considerable difficulties in presenting the true beauty of gem materials effectively in this book.

An illustration of a natural history collection containing gems, minerals, fossils and other natural curios, published in 1655. Photograph courtesy of C. Cavey.

Opposite: *A superb group photograph, showing a hand-coloured 19th-century engraved book illustration, crystals, glass crystal models, fossils, books on minerals, and three bronze medals won for mineral exhibits in the 19th century. Photograph courtesy of B.S. Lloyd of Gregory, Bottley & Lloyd.*

INTRODUCTION

The intention of this book is to provide a general introduction to the world of gems and jewels. The subject is a very large and complex one, as virtually every major culture since the dawn of time has had its own beliefs and uses for gems. Many were found locally, but perilous journeys were made for stones to far distant places, and for these a great price had to be paid. Fabulous stories were invented of amazing monsters and perils to dissuade the treasure-seeker from embarking on the paths to the mining areas.

In this modern era, where air travel, medicines and hospitals are commonplace, it is hard to imagine how difficult it was to obtain certain gems. Only 100 years ago, it often took many months of dangerous travel, and the risk of horrible disease and infection, to gain a small number of stones from their source.

A phenomenal number of beliefs are still attached to stones, and their virtues are still being used to treat innumerable ailments in virtually all parts of the globe. Recently a great revival of interest in natural gem crystals has come from the USA, and many people find wearing them calming and beneficial, and use them as a focus for meditation to help escape the general stresses of modern living.

As we proceed through this book we will look at the common gemstones from many different points of view, and briefly examine some of their many uses and the beliefs attached to them. No attempt is made here to describe the vast numbers of rare and obscure gems that have largely been identified in the last 100 years. Readers are referred to the bibliographical section of this book where there are a number of books listed to facilitate further research. References are, however, made to a few gemstones which proved to be new species when they were closely examined.

The scope of this book encompasses a varied approach to gems, and the different sections deal with the subject in a number of ways. Historical ideas rarely go "hand in glove" with modern scientific research into the actual provable properties of the gems, but in some cases there are rather interesting facts which give credence to some of the beliefs, and these are referred to and listed where possible in the main gemstone section.

Gemstones are also dealt with scientifically and references are made to man-made copies (synthetic gems) and imitation gemstones in an attempt to introduce the reader to this very complex and scientific area. Warnings and advice are given on the hazards and problems that can be encountered when gem material is purchased.

A section on the history and use of carved and engraved gems is included as an introduction to this fascinating subject. Julius Caesar, Catherine the Great, Napoleon, Wellington, and many of the major personalities who feature in the history of the Western world were all keen collectors of engraved gems. What happened to kill this interest in the early part of the nineteenth century? Why, today, can you buy some of the greatest treasures held by crown princes and kings for a matter of a few hundred pounds? These and other questions are discussed.

Fine modern gem carvings are examined and a guide provided to their workmanship and execution. There is a detailed discussion of the methods of research, finish and techniques which the modern carver can employ when working on the most delicate of stones. Mention is made of the pioneering work of Peter Carl Fabergé in popularizing gemstone carvings in the early twentieth century. There are also profiles of the English carver Alfred Pocock (who worked for Fabergé from 1905 to 1914) who expanded the oriental ideals of carving gem materials in shapes and forms according to their natural form, shape and colour, and of the modern carver Gerd Dreher of Idar-Oberstein in West Germany, who represents the fourth generation in his family to carve gems. He has taken the art to yet further heights with the application of traditional skills and the use of the latest modern techniques and equipment.

The illustrations are taken from a number of sources but my chief design has been to show as many examples as possible of gemstones and unusual jewels which would otherwise be totally inaccessible to the reader.

Opposite: *An extraordinary group of sea horses carved in chrysocolla quartz, skilfully utilizing the green malachite and white crystalline quartz in the one piece of natural material. Gold fins and a polished rock crystal base are added for further effect. Carving by G. Dreher. Photograph courtesy of P.V. Keane.*

Gems

The majority of gemstones are relatively simple chemical compounds, which form part of the mineral kingdom. The simplest substances known to man are the elements, which go to make up ourselves, our planet, and all the things around us. Only one gemstone is a pure element, and this, surprisingly enough, is the same element that is the basis of virtually all life on our planet. The element is carbon, and the gemstone is diamond.

Carbon is not only found in nature as diamond, but also occurs as the mineral graphite (one of the softest materials known to man), with which most people are familiar as the "lead" in pencils. It is very curious that inorganic carbon forms both the hardest and almost the softest of all mineral materials, without any permutations in between. Nearly all life forms on our planet contain organic carbon, and mixtures of this carbon and other elements make up the bulk of living creatures. Organic gemstones such as amber are hydrocarbons.

A mineral by definition is inorganic, and has a definite chemical composition, structure, and properties that vary only within defined limits. Rocks, on the other hand, are mixtures of minerals, and these can vary considerably in their make-up both within the one piece or in a number of pieces. Only a few gem materials can be defined as rocks – the best known of these is probably lapis-lazuli.

Contrary to popular art teaching and a number of other misconceptions, minerals in nature frequently grow in straight lines and have very pure symmetrical forms. The reader is advised to look closely at the

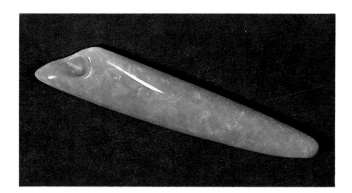

A polished black opal, which is a fossilized replacement of a belemnite. Whole dinosaurs that have been replaced by precious opal are known, but are very rare. Photograph by E.A. Jobbins.

pictures of natural crystals in this work, as many of these show a high degree of perfection of form.

To enable mineralogists to categorize minerals, several systems were introduced. The primary method of classification is still by basic chemical formula. The elements are dealt with first, and then compounds of the elements are segregated into separate sections the more complex they become. After the minerals have been arranged in this way, they are then examined in order to break them down still further into different materials. This may seem unnecessarily complex, but there are a few gemstones that have exactly the same chemical make-up but are completely different in all other ways.

The internal arrangement of the atoms that form many gem materials are mirrored in the outward shape of the various crystals that they go to create. These shapes always reflect the internal forces that are at work within each and every crystalline gemstone.

The crystal shape of the gem will give the gemmologist a great deal of information; and these shapes are broken down for convenience into seven basic crystal systems, which have been devised to help identify gems when they come in recognizable shapes. Stones of one type will only form crystals of a particular range of shapes. By closely examining the materials in this way it is possible to identify many materials purely by their outward appearance. This may at first seem rather unnecessary, but the sheer cost of employing destructive or expensive laboratory testing methods on valuable gem material can be prohibitive.

The seven crystal systems are based on imaginary

An engraved plate showing diamond cutting and polishing in London, dated 1730. Photograph courtesy of C. Cavey.

Opposite: *A superb crystal group of amethyst on matrix, from Vera Cruz, Mexico. Photograph courtesy of B.S. Lloyd of Gregory, Bottley & Lloyd.*

A man lifting gravel from a gem pit in Ratnapura, Sri Lanka. Photograph courtesy of E.A. Jobbins.

lines (axes) which pass through the crystal and match up with its shape, much like putting a round peg in a round hole. The systems have names which relate to their shapes, and they become less symmetrical as they are looked at in the following order.

The cubic is the most symmetrical of the crystal systems. It has three axes, all of which are equal in length and intersect at 90 degrees. All gemstones that form in this system have optical properties that do not vary with the direction from which they are viewed.

Tetragonal is less symmetrical than cubic. Crystals of this kind also have three axes all intersecting at 90 degrees, but only two of these are equal, while the third can be of any length. They are usually either shorter or longer in one direction than the other.

Hexagonal has four axes, three of which intersect at 60 degrees while the fourth is variable but intersects the other three at 90 degrees. These crystals come in six-sided columns which can be elongated or flattened.

Trigonal has the same four axes as hexagonal, but the fourth axis has three-fold symmetry, rather than sixfold.

Tetragonal, hexagonal, and trigonal gems can all be two different colours if viewed from different directions.

Orthorhombic crystals have three axes that intersect at 90 degrees but all of them are unequal.

Monoclinic crystals have three axes of unequal length, two of which intersect at 90 degrees.

Triclinic crystals have three axes, all of which are unequal and cut one another obliquely.

Orthorhombic, monoclinic and triclinic crystals can have three different colours in three different directions.

The physical properties of gemstones are not only an important aid in their identification, but are the very reasons why these materials are classified as gemstones.

Above all, gem materials should be hard enough to withstand some degree of wear when mounted in jewellery. The mineralogist Friedrich Mohs devised a scale of hardness in the eighteenth century in an attempt to improve the classification of minerals and gemstones. Although this table is inconsistent it is still useful in giving an indication of the relationship in hardness of one gem to another.

Mohs' Scale of Hardness

Talc	=	1	Orthoclase	=	6
Gypsum	=	2	Quartz	=	7
Calcite	=	3	Topaz	=	8
Fluorite	=	4	Corundum	=	9
Apatite	=	5	Diamond	=	10

The scale is misleading as the difference in hardness of the various stones is far from equal. To illustrate this point, it can be noted that the actual difference between 1 and 9 is less than the difference between 9 and 10.

Hardness-testing is used most commonly on rough material and rarely on finished gemstones. Having to

A selection of naturally fancy-coloured diamonds weighing between 0.57 and 1.93 carats. Photograph courtesy of E.A. Jobbins.

repolish an expensive gem because of a careless hardness test can be very costly.

Various other physical properties of gemstones are examined by gemmologists when they seek to identify gem material. The complexities of this subject preclude its inclusion here, but the reader is referred to the bibliographical section at the end of this book for specialized works on this subject.

Common gem materials have been used by mankind since the dawn of history, and gems have also been known to be ground, cut, carved and polished from the Ancient Egyptian period. A number of examples of these can be seen in major museums throughout the world. The art of cutting gems is known as the

The gem mines at Mogok, Upper Burma. Photograph courtesy of E.A. Jobbins.

art of the lapidary. It is thought that gems were first cut by relatively primitive methods, and cutting by these processes still continues today in remote areas of the world.

Hardness is very important when cutting gems, because they are some of the hardest substances known to man. Many gem materials are tougher than the hardest steel blades, which are usually just below 7 on Mohs' scale. Gem material was worked by grinding hard but poor-quality gems into powders, which were then fed onto a soft metal wheel or wire. With the application of a liquid, either water or oil, some of this powder would adhere to the wheel or wire, which would then grind or cut the softer stone brought into contact with it.

Polishing stones is carried out using various metal oxides; today diamond powder is usually the preferred polishing agent of the lapidary. Synthetically produced abrasives are principally employed in the stone-cutting industries, since they are cheap, effective, and have a consistency rarely available in natural material.

The mining of gem materials has been shrouded in mystery for many thousands of years, and it was not until the beginning of the nineteenth century that any number of reliable facts were published relating to the occurrence of gems. Today the source, geology and occurrence of all the known principal gem deposits in the world are well catalogued.

Gemstones (excluding organic materials) are usually found in old rock formations, although there are a few exceptions, such as opal. Many gems are found in remote inaccessible areas, while some have been discovered in the most unlikely places. There are gem deposits in the granites of Manhattan Island, New York, although it is not a practical proposition to mine for them there.

There are places in South America and Africa where major gem mines have been discovered by accident when the land was ploughed for farming. The immense diamond fields of South Africa were only exploited after the visiting friend of a local farmer obtained a diamond from the farmer's son who, in turn, had exchanged it for a few marbles with a friend. It took some time for people to become convinced of the significance of this find, for some authorities of the day denied that the stone was indeed a diamond!

Extreme care has to be taken when potential new gem deposits are discovered. The practice of "salting" mines (depositing gem material in a locality) has certainly cost many investors their money, so claims have to be examined very carefully.

The only gemstone that is commercially mined on a large scale is diamond. The industry is largely controlled by one organization (the Central Selling Organization) that mines or buys in material whch is then graded and distributed. A large proportion (approximately 80 per cent) of the world's diamond supplies are controlled in this way. It has been argued that diamonds would be considerably cheaper if there were a free market. The evidence from the mining of other gems strongly contradicts these suggestions.

The sheer investment required to mine any substance on a commercial scale is enormous. Hundreds of millions of dollars have to be ploughed into new mining projects, some of which will prove to be totally fruitless. Hopefully one or two of the projects may yield sufficient profits to compensate for the losses of the others, and occasionally some will be so productive as to bring very substantial returns.

Virtually all the mining specifically for other gem materials is conducted by relatively primitive methods. Apart from the occasional use of explosives, small bulldozers and digging machines, much of gem-mining is carried out by pick, spade and shovel, by small numbers of men working on the ground.

A natural uncut ruby in calcite matrix, with a cut ruby of 1.25 carats. The ruby is from the Hunza Valley, Pakistan, and the cut gemstone is of Burmese origin. Photograph courtesy of C. Cavey.

Many gemstones are easier to extract by the "hands on" methods for, hard as they are, they can be brittle and fracture easily. One good example is emerald-mining. These stones are very brittle but very firmly attached to the surrounding rock, and many are broken and shattered during the mining process. This reduces the potential yield during extraction.

Some hard material, such as sapphire, is often found as water-worn pebbles in old rivers and stream beds. Large-scale mechanical extraction techniques can be used for this material, but identification, sorting, and grading all has to be done by hand. The principal countries and sources of the most important commercial gem materials are given in the main gem section.

It is probably true to say the world gem markets would find it difficult to support large-scale mining, as the increased yield from such production would outstrip the demand for the various gem materials.

Today it is possible to produce virtually all gem-stones artificially in laboratories. Man-made gems are called synthetics, a term applied only to materials that have the same composition and properties as the natural gemstone. Synthetic rubies and natural rubies, for example, are both hardness 9, and both have a similar crystal form. It is only by examining their internal structures and inclusions that the synthetics can be differentiated from the natural gems. A few synthetic products have been manufactured that do

not have any natural counterpart, and these are merely known by their own names.

Jewels

A jewel may be defined as an ornament containing a precious stone or stones. Today the term has been applied to many things (watch jewels, for example, are bearings made from gem material) but it still primarily refers to a precious object, usually worn for adorn-ment. It is common prac-tice among present-day gem dealers to dispense with the old terms "pre-cious" and "semi-pre-cious" stones. The first of these was used in the past exclusively to de-scribe diamonds, rubies, sapphires, emeralds, pearls, and occasionally opals. All other gem-stones were classified as semi-precious. As many

A discoloured nephrite jade dragon pendant. Chinese, approximately 1100 B.C. Photograph courtesy of E.A. Jobbins.

semi-precious" gemstones grossly exceed the lower quality "precious" stones in value, it is now usual to refer to all gem materials as gemstones.

A jewel can be made purely from one large worked gemstone, or it can be fashioned from precious metal and set with gemstones. Precious metal objects of fine workmanship which contain no gems may also some-times be classified as jewels. The word jewel seems to have been derived from the word "joy", and it is still a joy today to be the owner of a jewel.

The use of gems in jewels is catalogued throughout the history of mankind, although the truly magnifi-cent precious objects we see in museums today were principally made for the exclusive use of a few noble families. Many of these surviving examples were items buried with their owners, some no doubt because they were favourite pieces that had been treasured by the wearers during their lifetimes, others made exclusive-ly for decoration after burial, to judge from their fragile nature and delicate construction.

Jewels played an important part in the daily lives of

noble families. They were worn not only to display the wealth, authority and power of their owners, but to protect them against all manner of diseases, poisoning, and betrayal. Many of these items were carefully designed both to conform to the fashions of the day, and to incorporate combinations of gemstones, ciphers, and magical inscriptions, all of which were intended to protect and bring benefit to the wearer.

When Egypt was part of the Roman Empire, a pseudo-Christian sect developed, known as the gnostics. Gems and jewels were made by these people for virtually any purpose. Tailor-made jewels were produced for setting in horses' bridles, supposedly to enable them to win their races; others were made as charms to entice lovers; and some were made to bring death, destruction and evil upon all who possessed them. Jewels were certainly worn, sometimes in great numbers, and references exist to Roman emperors being covered from head to foot in hundreds of them.

The practice of setting gems in the crowns of kings seems to have become popular in the early medieval period. Certainly, virtually all the surviving crown jewels have had many gems set in them. Diamonds were rarely used until methods of cutting them were developed in the fourteenth century, although other gems continued to be more popular right up to the

Above: *A portrait of Queen Mary I of England, by Moro. Note the jewels in the head-dress, round the neck, round the waist, on both wrists, and the two rings visible. Her half-sister and successor, Elizabeth 1st developed the fashion of wearing many jewels, on all parts of the costume. Circa 1533. Photograph courtesy of C. Cavey.*

Below: *An engraving of a scene featuring Fredrick III, Elector of Brandenburg, reviewing his collection of engraved gems, coins, medals, and sculpture. Germany, 1696. Photograph courtesy of C. Cavey.*

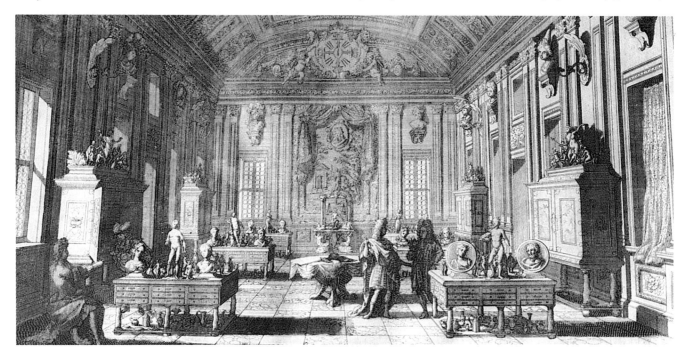

seventeenth century. With the discovery of the Americas and the beginning of the Renaissance, trade blossomed in the European world. Elizabeth I of England wore dresses encrusted with over a hundred gem-set jewels, in between which were quantities of pearls all strung and sewn in complex patterns. Diamonds were purchased in India from the Mogul emperors, and many other wonderful gemstones became available to the jewellers and craftsmen, in quantity, for the first time.

As wealth spread with the increase in trade, fashions changed more often. New ideas, fabric and designs were coming from the East, and the wealthy wanted the latest up-to-date designs, not only in their clothes,

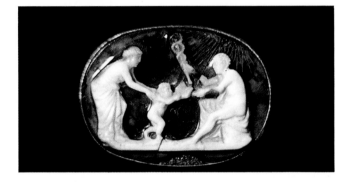

Classical cameo, showing Venus introducing Cupid to Mercury to learn the ways of man. Circa 1st century A.D., mount 18th century. Formerly in the collection of the Duke of Wellington. Photograph courtesy of C. Cavey.

but also in their jewellery. The bright coloured enamels of the fifteenth and sixteenth centuries, were replaced by more subdued and subtle colours. Gemstones then became brighter and more striking in their appearance because of improvements in cutting techniques and a better understanding of the correct angles suitable for faceting each gem. By the eighteenth century diamonds were the most revered of gems, and they were used in all forms of jewels, from decorative hairpieces to gem-set buttons.

During the Renaissance there was an increased interest in the classical Greek and Roman periods, and by the seventeenth century it was common practice for all European monarchs of the period to be portrayed in the manner and dress of Roman emperors in statues and on coinage. By the eighteenth century it had become even more fashionable to collect all things classical, and the most comprehensive range of classi-

cal art survived on engraved gemstones. These collections were the pride of emperors, kings, and noblemen throughout Europe.

When Napoleon I was crowned Emperor of France and her provinces, he had a very simple crown made. This contradicted the fashion of the day, as it was set with classical cameos and intaglios. Initially this may seem a strange choice, but Napoleon had ambitions of reviving the Roman Empire, which he saw as a civilizing stable influence lasting over 1000 years. By associating himself with the most potent surviving emblems of classical nobility, he was trying to create a powerful image of himself as a great leader and emperor of his people.

Prior to the nineteenth century jewellery was certainly held in very high regard. It was probably the simplest means in those days of transferring large amounts of money from one place to another. A large number of the gems and jewels owned by King

A strangely decayed pearl mounted as a pendant. This was unearthed in 1912 from the floor of a house in Cheapside, London. It had probably been buried since the middle of the 17th century and formed part of what is now known as the Cheapside hoard. Photograph courtesy of E.A. Jobbins.

Opposite: *A finely-made art nouveau pendant set with gemstones and enamel by the French jeweller Vever, circa 1900. Photograph courtesy of E.A. Jobbins.*

17

Charles I were sold to finance the English Civil War.

By the nineteenth century jewellery had become available to far more people as the Industrial Revolution brought increased prosperity. Mass-production techniques were now employed in the manufacture of basic items, and stones were cut to precise sizes to fit these settings. Hand-made jewellery also underwent a revival, and new techniques and styles were born. A fresh interest in the Renaissance style of jewellery was followed by the birth in France of the "art nouveau" style. This started with an attempt to revive the naturalist styles reminiscent of the medieval period.

At the beginning of the twentieth century a number of designers and craftsmen were developing a new range of styles. In Paris the new art movements had an increasing effect upon the jewellery industry. The famous glass-maker R. Lalique started his career by creating superbly detailed pieces of jewellery, at the very pinnacle of art nouveau design. Finding that

A signed portrait intaglio of superb quality. The double portrait represents Shakespeare and Garrick (a famous 18th-century actor), and was engraved by the famous English engraver Edmund Burch. Mounted in gold fob, and made in the late 18th century. Photograph courtesy of C. Cavey.

many weeks had to go into the design and modelling of one piece of jewellery, he went on to produce a range of moulded decorative glass.

In Russia at the beginning of the twentieth century there was considerable disposable wealth, and this created an ideal environment for the jewellery and decorative arts industries to flourish. A number of famous jewellery houses had shops and workshops in the Russian capital of St Petersburg. One house, run by Peter Carl Fabergé, who had developed and expanded his father's business, was destined to become a famous household name. In the extensive search to provide his wide range of wealthy clients with interesting gifts, *objets d'art* and jewels, he studied many designs and art forms from all over the world. The workshops and Fabergé's craftsmen produced an enormous range of silverware, jewellery, stone carvings and other decorative items. The time, skill and technical devotion of his workforce resulted in some of the most amazing jewels.

In the early 1920s, art nouveau was succeeded by a style that was to become known as "art deco". This was of a more angular nature, and many famous jewels were made between 1920–40. The last few decades have produced a large number of fine

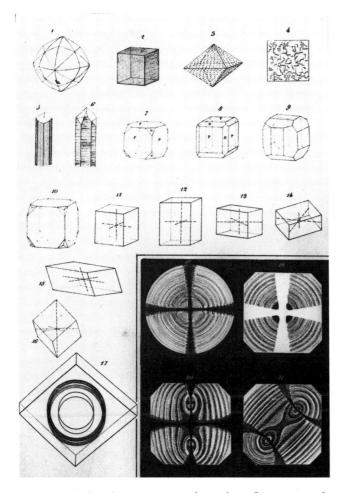

An engraved plate showing a range of crystals. In figures 11–16 the basic crystal forms have their imaginary axes drawn in. Figures 18–21 represent figures seen when minerals are examined under polarized light 1859. Photograph courtesy of C. Cavey.

Opposite: *A group of fine-quality modern jewellery, and a range of loose diamonds, rubies, sapphires, and emeralds. Photograph courtesy of Patrick Aldridge, Gemcut SA, Geneva.*

An engraving representing a classical sardonyx intaglio, which was in the collection of the Duke of Marlborough. This is engraved with the twelve signs of the Zodiac, and the goddess of victory in her chariot. 1768. Photograph courtesy of C. Cavey.

jewellery designers. The techniques, materials, equipment and range of technology that are now available have enabled a broader range of styles to develop.

Contrary to belief, the skill and ability to make finely detailed and intricate jewellery is alive and well. The relatively limited number of fine pieces of jewellery manufactured today relates solely to current fashion trends and the reluctance, mainly for security reasons, of people to wear very valuable items about their persons.

Agate portrait of Edward VI, King of England, circa 1550. Photograph courtesy of C. Cavey.

Birthstones

The origin of the belief that certain gemstones were of talismanic value to people born in particular months of the year dates back to the first century AD. These were catalogued by a writer named "Josephus", who

An 18th-century oil painting depicting a scene from the Bible. This depicts an encounter between Eli and Samuel, and it shows clearly the Jewish High Priest wearing his gem-set Breast-plate. Photograph courtesy of C. Cavey.

A Derbyshire black marble inlaid dish; the green-coloured gem material is malachite. Photograph courtesy of E.A. Jobbins.

An illustration of medieval mining for minerals and gem material, showing shafts, ladders, trucks, and other equipment used at the period. Photograph courtesy of C. Cavey.

The diamond mines at Kimberley in 1876, showing the progress made in excavation. The wires seen across the mine are to separate individual claims. It was not until later that the mine came under single ownership. Photograph courtesy of C. Cavey.

appears to have been the first author on this subject. St Jerome wrote about birthstones in the fifth century and compared these twelve gems to those set in the breastplate of the Jewish High Priest. Although references can be found in earlier literature, however, there is substantial evidence to support the belief that there was little serious interest in wearing birthstones before the eighteenth century.

There is some confusion surrounding the exact stones that are specifically attributed to each month, and these tend to vary from country to country. To add to the bewilderment there are also gems attributed to the twelve signs of the Zodiac, and these again vary from the monthly stones.

The origins of the beliefs surrounding these gems were developed further when the Book of Revelations gained popularity. This work mentions twelve magical gems in the construction of the "New Jerusalem". Certainly, the belief in stones having specific virtues for people born in certain months is very old.

The problem of ascribing a specific gem to a month of the year or sign of the Zodiac seems to be primarily related to the colour of the stone, and secondly to its underlying properties. Certain gems were chosen because the colours of the stones had a relationship to the character of the months. One possible reason, therefore, why there is such a variation in these stones is that the weather patterns, crops, and cycle of life vary in the different countries. Birthstones often alter from state to state within the USA, and many regional differences occur throughout Europe.

There are numerous zodiacal and astrological gems, and these have been used to focus planetary influences for many thousands of years. To add to the virtue of some of these stones, constellations, planetary symbols and numerical arrangements relating to planetary positions have been engraved into the surface of such gems.

Ancient Chinese symbolical weapons made of jade were often engraved with stellar formations, and so were many ancient Babylonian and Assyrian gems. Ancient Greek and Roman astrological stones are among the most popular subjects used during the classical period. Jewels that have elements in their designs relating to signs of the Zodiac are known from the medieval period. The custom of wearing charms still survives in many parts of the globe today. These are cut in precious metal or stone to represent a particular zodiacal sign.

DIAMOND

The name diamond was derived from the Greek word *adamas*, which has been translated as invincible or unconquerable. There is evidence that this name was also applied to the colourless variety of corundum (or sapphire), as gem-testing in the ancient world was a rather haphazard affair. Testing for true *adamas* usually took the form of placing the stone on a metal anvil and striking it several times with a hammer, to see if it would withstand the blows. Colourless sapphire and dia-mond could, under the right circumstances, survive this treatment; however, many genuine stones were no doubt broken in the process.

Today we connect the intrinsic hardness suggested by the name *adamas* with only one gemstone: the true diamond. Diamond is often represented on a standard of hardness devised by Friedrich Mohs in the early nineteenth century, which grades stones on a scale of 1 to 10. On this scale sapphire is 9 and diamond 10, but since the difference between the hardness of 1 and 9 is less than the difference between 9 and 10, these figures can be misleading.

CHEMICAL COMPOSITION: nearly pure Carbon, often with minute traces of elements such as Nitrogen, Boron, and so on. Diamond is the only gemstone which is a pure element and not a compound.

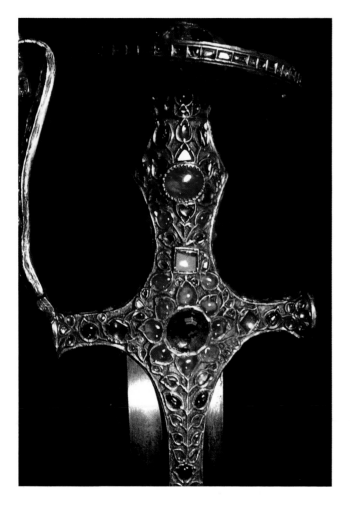

A gold-hilted sword, set with rubies, emeralds and diamonds, presented to Sir John Malcolm in 1812. Indian, late 18th century. Photograph courtesy of E.A. Jobbins.

An assortment of diamonds in their rough uncut state, showing a wide range of colours and shapes. These vary from a fraction of a carat to 9 carats in weight. Photograph courtesy of C. Cavey.

Strangely, Carbon is also the base element of nearly all the life forms on the planet, which may help to explain why mankind has always found the diamond so uniquely interesting.

COLOURS: nearly every known colour, although intense attractive colours are relatively rare. The rarest colour found in nature is intense bright red, and only a very few stones of any size have been recorded. The commonest colours are off-white to pale yellow and light brown. Diamonds that change appearance under different light sources are known, and some will convert the invisible ultra-violet light rays in daylight into a visible light and fluoresce. Some stones that appear colourless under the incandescent light of a standard light bulb may take on a distinct blue sheen in daylight. These are known in the trade as "over-blues". Some brown diamonds will have fine clouds of

Rough and cut diamonds showing the dispersive qualities of the gem material when fashioned from the rough. Photograph courtesy of Jacobs Lack Archutowski, Bond Street Antique Centre, 124 New Bond Street, London .

dust-like particles inside them, which will fluoresce green in daylight, changing the apparent colour of the stone. It has been noted that certain rare diamonds will also change colour according to their temperature. When taken from a cold safe after being locked up overnight, for example, certain stones which look yellow will shortly afterwards turn green. The cause of colour in gemstones is a very complex subject, and the reader is referred to the Bibliography for further reading on this topic.

CRYSTAL SYSTEM: cubic.

HABIT: most commonly octahedral (hence diamond-shaped), but frequently distorted, flattened, twinned

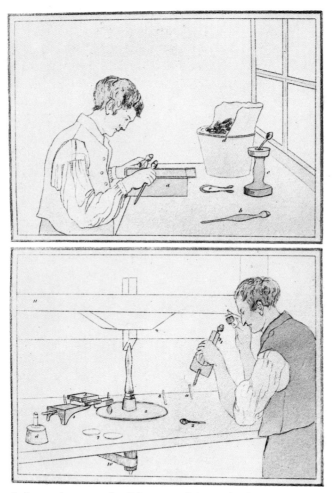

A photograph of the largest gem-quality diamond ever found, the "Star of Africa", or "Cullinan diamond". It weighed over 3000 carats, and was cut into nine principal stones. The largest stone (now in the British Crown Jewels) weighs 530.2 carats. Photograph courtesy of C. Cavey.

A diamond cutter and polisher at work in London in 1823. Photograph courtesy of C. Cavey.

and mixed forms, and sometimes complex clusters of many intergrowing crystals occur.
HARDNESS: 10.
CUT: normally faceted in a variety of cuts, of which the most common is the standard brilliant cut, although sometimes cut into extraordinary shapes by laser. Rarely engraved, but a few historical stones exist engraved with the names of their owners. Others are coats of arms and heraldic devices incised for use as seal matrices.

History

Curiously, there are few ancient pieces of jewellery set with the current "king of gems", and it is very probable that true diamond of any size was an extremely scarce material in the ancient world.

Adamas was one of the gemstones set in the breastplate of the Biblical Jewish High Priest, but there is good evidence to suggest that the name here probably refers to a softer stone than true diamond, more probably a colourless sapphire, or even the relatively common colourless topaz. All the stones in the breastplate were engraved with one of the names of the twelve tribes of Israel, and it is very unlikely that the ability to engrave or even polish diamond in any way was known before the fourteenth century AD. The High Priest used the *adamas* for reaching legal decisions. If he perceived the stone to be dim and lack-lustre then judgement was given against the case being brought, while if it was seen to be brilliant and to "shine out", then judgement was for the case.

Diamond was probably first used as a tool for incising and cutting other gemstones, and its immense hardness makes it extremely effective for this purpose. The ancient Greeks believed that the only way the *adamas* could be broken was by steeping it in goats' blood, after which it would break easily. The proximity of a diamond to a lodestone (a naturally magnetic mineral) supposedly made the lodestone lose its powers. Both these abilities have been disproved by many researchers.

Up until the eighteenth century diamond was thought to be extremely poisonous, a property that those who owned or mined the stones no doubt wished to promote. Since a favourite and effective means of stealing a diamond was to swallow it whole and wait a few days for it to pass through the digestive system, the myth that it was poisonous presumably deterred many from the attempt. Diamond powder was supposedly even more deadly, but it would appear that the principal toxic component of the powder was probably added arsenic.

A curious incident ocurred in the history of the famous Great Sancy diamond. This gem was being carried by a trusted servant as collateral for finance in a war taking place in late sixteenth-century Europe. The servant was set upon, robbed and killed, but the stone was later recovered from the unfortunate man's stomach. Loyal to his master, he had swallowed it, and although the thieves had stripped his body they had failed to find the precious gem.

Diamond was used extensively as an amulet to ward

off evil, particularly the "evil eye", probably because of its immense strength and the superb lustre, which will reflect light most effectively, dazzling the darkness of evil. It was a potent charm for victory in battle, as the invincible nature of the stone was said to "rub off" on the wearer. The stone was often employed in the East as the third eye of idols. Indeed, many historical gems were used for this purpose.

With the advent of modern scientific methods in the nineteenth century it became easier to analyse minerals, and many of the superstitions surrounding gems were closely examined. This did not, however, stop some of the wealthy natives of India from having diamond powder applied to their teeth in an attempt to repair decay. The powder supposedly also had the means to protect people from lightning.

In modern crystal healing, diamond is used by some schools as stone to increase spiritual consciousness and awareness.

Sources

Diamond was first found and mined in the Golconda area of India, and a few stones were also imported from Borneo. These were the only two sources known to the ancient world, and it was not until the seventeenth century that a new supply was discovered in the gold diggings in Brazil. At that time diamond was not the principal gemstone, being ranked third in desirability after ruby and emerald. Diamond-cutting on a commercial scale was developed in the fourteenth to fifteenth centuries, but material was hard to obtain, since the acquisition of diamond at that time frequently involved an extremely perilous journey.

In the sixteenth century Jean Baptiste Tavernier brought back to France a number of the principal diamonds of the day from his epic travels to the eastern courts. Later, in the early seventeenth century, Sir Paul Pindar returned to England from a period as ambassador to Turkey with several fine large diamonds, which he sold to King Charles I.

With the exploration of Brazil diamond became available to Europeans in considerable quantities for the first time, and the techniques of cutting improved so that it grew to be a more popular gemstone. Since it is colourless the stone was not limited by the fashionable colour preferences of the day and could be worn to complement most forms of court dress. Like most other gems, diamonds were owned chiefly by a select group of the rich and famous. It was not until the

Left: *An unusual cross, set on both sides with rose and table-cut diamonds, which are silver foiled on the reverse (diamonds cut in this primitive way have been produced in India since the 14th century). The metal is high-quality gold and there is coloured enamelled decoration along its edges. Hyderabad, India, circa 1750. Photograph courtesy of C. Cavey.*

Right: *An extraordinary picture agate set in a 17th-century silver, diamond-set, miniature frame. Sometimes agates can rival the work of good artists in their markings and pictorial qualities. Photograph courtesy of C. Cavey.*

An extraordinary flat-cut diamond weighing 56.71 carats. It is certainly of Indian origin, and is typical of gems worn by the Mogul Emperors in the early 17th century. It is now named the Javeri Diamond. Photograph courtesy of E.A. Jobbins.

second half of the nineteenth century, when the rich diamond fields of South Africa were discovered, that diamonds could be owned by the common people. The Industrial Revolution had brought prosperity to many, and for the first time diamonds were within reach of a large section of the community.

The two principal sources of diamonds today have been exploited only comparatively recently. Although Australia was a known diamond locality in the nineteenth century, it was not until the 1970s that sufficient investment in plant and machinery took place to realize its full potential. The diamond mines of the USSR are among the most productive suppliers of gems in the world and yield quantities of fine-grade gemstones, but since no definitive figures are released by the Soviet government it is hard to be certain of the true scale of production. There are also a number of African countries which produce substantial quantities of diamond, several localities in the USA, and innumerable small deposits elsewhere which have yet to be exploited on a fully commercial basis.

Diamonds are usually found in one of two kinds of site. The oldest and most common is among the gravels of very old river beds. In these cases the diamonds have been carried out of the mother rock by erosion and left in the river beds. Until the discovery of the deposits in Kimberley, South Africa, all diamond was found in such sources.

At Kimberley the diamond was found in the pipes of a long extinct volcano. This was the first time that the stone was mined from its mother rock, and such extraction from source pipes now also takes place in Siberia, Australia and Botswana.

Treatment of Diamonds

Diamonds have been artificially coloured by exposure to a variety of radiation sources and in some cases by subsequent heat treatment as well. Nowadays they may also be infilled with glass to hide fissures and cracks.

The diamond mines at Kimberley, South Africa, during its early open-cast workings in 1872. Photograph courtesy of C. Cavey.

The re-cutting of the Koh-i-Noor diamond supervised by the Duke of Wellington, 1852. Photograph courtesy of C. Cavey.

Charles I, King of England, Jewel. An engraved diamond-set frame, containing a portrait of his wife Henrietta Maria. Photograph courtesy of C. Cavey.

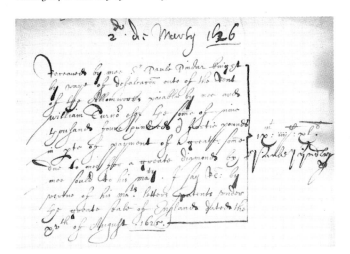

A receipt, acknowledging a part payment by King Charles I for a diamond he purchased for £25,000.00, in 1625. The diamond was later sold in France to help finance the English Civil War. Photograph courtesy of C. Cavey.

Two superb diamond-set rings – the principal diamonds are over 20 carats in size. The top stone is emerald-cut and has triangular-cut diamonds on its shoulders. The principal diamond in the lower ring is set with tapered baguette-cut diamonds on its shoulders. Photograph courtesy of Patrick Aldridge, Gemcut SA, Geneva.

A crystal group of the man-made abrasive silicon carbide, which is ground up and sold under the name of "Carborundum". Rough crystalline pieces of this material are occasionally encountered in jewellery. Its hardness is 9.25! Photograph courtesy of C. Cavey.

A large (over 40 carats) fancy-cut natural yellow diamond. Photograph courtesy of Patrick Aldridge, Gemcut SA, Geneva.

Synthetic Diamonds

True synthetic diamond has been manufactured since the 1950s in the USA, where the General Electric Company first pioneered its commercial production. A quantity of this material has been produced every year for use in a range of industrial manufacturing processes. A small number of gem-quality crystals were also produced but were found to be too costly to make on a commercial basis.

A number of companies throughout the world are currently working on the creation of synthetic diamond, but most are attempting to make a product for specialist markets. Gem-quality synthetic diamonds suitable for cutting are of a brownish yellow colour and can easily be identified as synthetic by established gem-testing laboratories. A new type of extremely pure stone, the carbon 12 diamond, is now being produced as a high-temperature heat sink for microscopic electronic components. Since this type is 50 per cent more heat-conductive than conventional diamond, it is hoped that it will enable electronics manufacturers to make much smaller circuits. At present there is no intention to produce these stones in sufficient size for the gemstone market.

Principal Gemstones that Can Simulate Diamonds

GLASS (PASTE): used for many years as a diamond simulant, although not very convincing to the experienced eye.

ROCK CRYSTAL: harder than glass, but still a less than convincing simulant.

COLOURLESS TOPAZ: harder than rock crystal, although again not very convincing. In the rough, however, it has a similar specific gravity to diamond and can confuse the inexperienced.

NATURAL COLOURLESS ZIRCON: is bright, and in small sizes when freshly polished can be quite "diamond-like" in appearance. It is easy to identify with a jeweller's magnifying glass, or loupe, from its strong double refraction.

SPHALERITE (ZINC BLENDE): very soft and fragile, but has a refractive index closer to that of diamond than any other natural gemstones.

SPHENE: soft and very strongly doubly refractive.

SYNTHETIC CUBIC ZIRCONIA (CZ): currently the principal diamond simulant, is sold under many trade-names. Hard and durable, it is the most convincing simulant so far produced on a commercial basis. Although it is sometimes described by the uneducated salesperson as synthetic diamond, it is not. Synthetics must be almost identical both chemically and physically to their natural counterparts.

A number of synthetic stones made as diamond simulants were in circulation for a few years, but are rarely encountered on the modern market. They include Lithium Niobate; synthetic Rutile; Strontium Titanate; Yttrium Aluminium Garnet (YAG); and Gadolinium Gallium Garnet (GGG). For other gemstones which can look like diamonds, the reader is advised to consult specialist books on diamond.

RUBY

The word ruby was originally applied to a number of different gemstones. Each variety has its own name, which suggests that the gem merchants of the day were aware that they all had different properties.

The ancient Greeks used the term *anthrax* to describe the stone that glowed "flaming blood-red" like burning coal. This name has now been linked by scholars with the modern ruby.

CHEMICAL COMPOSITION: Aluminium Oxide, with sufficient Chromic Oxide to colour the stone to a distinct red.

COLOURS: the red variety of the mineral corundum, which in its pure state is colourless. Additional colouring elements produce virtually all colours, although these are classified as sapphires, rather than rubies. There is currently some debate over the definition of ruby, since pink sapphires can be of an almost identical chemical make-up. One way to decide the difference between ruby and pink sapphire is by applying the following definitions: rubies are red with a hint or shade of another colour or colours, the base colour of the stone remaining a rich red. Pink sapphires, on the other hand, are of a pink base colour but have intense flashes of red when fine.

A toad carved from a single piece of ruby; the whole item is over 3 inches across. The clever use of varying degrees of polish clearly distinguishes carving from base. Carved by G. Dreher. Photograph courtesy of P.V. Keane.

CRYSTAL SYSTEM: trigonal.

HABIT: usually flattened crystals with a hexagonal outline, but always with triangular growth markings on the terminal faces. There are many additional forms that range from elongated prisms, narrowing at each end, to extremely thin, flat, tabular plates.

HARDNESS: 9. In theory there should be no difference between the hardness of ruby and that of sapphire. However, the crystals of ruby frequently suffer from lammellar twinning, and this makes the gemstone easier to damage than many sapphires.

CUT: faceted, cut *en cabochon* (sometimes producing star stones), engraved and carved in a variety of ways.

History

The legends and stories surrounding the nature and properties of ruby are plentiful, and there are references to this gemstone in holy texts from all parts of the world.

Ruby was one of the stones supposedly used in the breastplate of the Jewish High Priest, although it is unlikely that the gem mentioned in the Bible is the same as that which we would call ruby today.

In the Hindu religion the ruby is ranked above all other gems, although many other similar stones may be accepted as varieties of ruby. The true ruby, as we now define it, is rarely encountered in early pieces of jewellery, and it would seem that its near cousin, the spinel, was the most common gemstone to which the general name "ruby" was applied. Indeed, red spinel was accepted as a type of ruby until the end of the nineteenth century, when stricter scientific classification confined the name to the red variety of corundum only. On close inspection virtually all the large rubies (over 10 carats) that have survived in crown jewels and private collections have been found to be red spinels. The probable reason for this lack of large rubies is that gem-quality stones are very rare, and that the kings of Burma, which is the main source of

A toad carved in ruby sitting on a zoisite leaf. Rubies from Tanzania come in a matrix of green zoisite rock, and this material has been utilized to optimum effect in this carving. Carved by G. Dreher. Photograph courtesy of G. Dreher.

fine gem ruby, for many centuries decreed that all the larger stones found were crown property. Any person found concealing such gems not only had them confiscated but risked summary execution.

The magical properties and virtues once associated with ruby can therefore also be attributed to a number of spinels and even to certain varieties of garnet and tourmaline. Rubies were worn by many people to keep them in good bodily and mental health. In the fourteenth century the stone was believed to bring peace and well-being to its owner, and to guard the house, fruit-trees and vineyards against tempest. The loss of such gems was frequently followed by catastrophe and great care was therefore taken to guard them well.

The ruby owes much of its magical and talismanic significance to its blood-like colour, and was even introduced into the flesh of the owner as protection from wounds and bleeding in battle. It would seem that this belief was enhanced by the fact that only the bravest soldiers were likely to endure the painful process of having the stone inserted under their skin. Supposed additional properties of rubies included the lighting of darkened rooms and the boiling of liquids in which they were placed. Rubies were also said to warn their owners of imminent peril by turning dark or black and not returning to their normal colour until the danger had passed.

In modern crystal healing, ruby is employed by some schools for relieving the symptoms of anaemia, for revitalizing people who suffer from poor blood circulation, for the relief of pain and cramp and for the prevention of miscarriage. The colour of the stone and its associations with blood and heat have made it an ideal material for use in such sympathetic magic over countless generations.

Sources

The rich deposits of the Mogok Stone Tract of Upper Burma have been the source of the world's finest rubies (and red spinels) since records began. The material is obtained in one of two ways: firstly, from the stream gravels, where it has been eroded out of the rocks and comes mixed with an assortment of other gemstones, some of which have been completely rounded by abrasion against each other over many millions of years. Secondly, rubies are mined from the calcite and limestone rocks in which they have undergone considerable heat and pressure. This probably explains why they are of such a fine colour, as the natural forces have frequently caused any iron in the rubies to be burnt out and expelled.

Rubies from the many mines in Thailand are generally regarded as inferior in colour to those from Burma. Most material from this source is found in stream gravels as water-worn pebbles, and the duller coloration is mainly due to quantities of iron being present as an impurity in the gems. It should be said, however, that many mines can occasionally produce very fine rubies, and that all produce poor-coloured and non-gem-quality material in great quantity. Rubies from Thailand were held in low esteem in the latter part of the nineteenth century and were extensively used in relatively low-cost jewellery.

Pakistan produces fine-coloured ruby from the deposits of the Hunza Valley. This is mined from a crystalline calcite rock and is very similar to the material from Burma. Large stones of gem quality are very rarely found, as the bulk of these gems are heavily fractured.

The largest and some of the most brilliant of the fine gem rubies come from Sri Lanka, although here they are usually found as a by-product of sapphire-mining. This country has produced a number of large star rubies, sometimes over 300 carats. Faceted gems from this source often owe their brilliant appearance to part of the stone being totally colourless. With expert cutting an intense area or patch of colour can flood the whole stone. Sri Lankan rubies are often cut with deep backs, or pavilions, both to achieve this effect and so that local jewellers can set the stone in such a way that it will touch the skin of the wearer. Without such contact, it is believed, the full beneficial effects of the stone would not be felt. Quantities of pink sapphire are also found in Sri Lanka.

Tanzania has produced the world's largest rubies to date, but virtually all this material is opaque and used mainly for carvings, many of which include the attractive bright-green zoisite rock, which affords a pleasing contrast. Crystals up to 12 inches across have been seen from this locality, some containing small transparent areas which occasionally produce intense red gem-quality rubies. A small quantity of fine pinkish-red stones, which can be very similar in appearance to

A 17th-century gold, enamel, and gem-set monstrance. Christ's portrait on the handkerchief of St. Veronica is portrayed by an engraved ruby in cameo. The crucifixion scene is represented by a carved sapphire, in cameo. Photograph courtesy of C. Cavey.

a range of Burmese material, has been found in Kenya; while Guinea produces quantities of large, dull-brownish-red star stones.

The mines at Jedalak in Afghanistan produce superb rubies of an extraordinary bright red but these are rarely of any notable size. Stones have been mined from this locality for several thousand years.

India has a very large deposit of ruby to the south of Mysore. The bulk of this material produces opaque, dull-red star rubies, which are used in relatively low-cost jewellery. Better-quality material is sometimes found, but it is hardly ever transparent. A great quantity of ruby is in fact imported into India for

consumption in its home market.

The state of North Carolina in the USA produces large masses of opaque ruby, small transparent areas of which are occasionally cut into gems. Small quantities of dark-red opaque rubies come from the Ural Mountains area of the USSR. In addition, Norway produces a quantity of finely crystallized but opaque ruby; and Australia flattish opaque red crystal from the Harts Mountain area of the Northern Territories.

Treatment of Natural Rubies

Many natural rubies are heat-treated by a variety of methods to improve their colour. This is done to remove "silk" (fine hair-like masses of rutile crystals) and iron from the stones. Glass-infilling of fisures and cracks is now used in an attempt to improve the appearance of inferior stones.

Synthetic Rubies

Synthetic rubies have been successfully manufactured in gem quality since the last years of the nineteenth century. The French chemist Auguste Verneuil developed a process of growing large transparent candle-shaped boules from powdered natural rubies. A small oxyhydrogen furnace is used to melt the falling powder and layers are then grown on to a seed crystal to build up the boule. Verneuil went on to develop a process of production from refined chemicals.

This type of synthetic ruby is cheap, quick and easy to produce, the whole process taking only a few hours. When they first appeared on the market enormous sums of money were paid for these stones, but it was not long before there was a major price crash for both ruby and sapphire.

By the 1930s a number of gemmologists had been trained to identify these synthetic gemstones, and the ruby market was beginning to recover, although many traders had gone out of business in the meantime. Since that time a number of other more complex synthetic rubies have been made, some as by-products

Opposite: A superb matching art deco ruby- and diamond-set necklace and bracelet. It can take years of searching the gem markets to match the quality, cut and colour of so many fine diamonds and rubies. Photograph courtesy of Patrick Aldridge, Gemcut SA, Geneva.

of commercial research into the laser properties of this gemstone. Today the bulk of synthetic ruby is still made by the Verneuil process, and much of this is used for various industrial purposes, such as the making of watch jewels. Doublets, consisting of a thin top layer of natural green sapphire and a base of synthetic ruby, are made in Thailand.

A superb pair of fine (pigeons blood) drop-shaped faceted Burmese rubies, set with marquise and drop-shaped diamonds. These earrings were made within the last fifty years. Rubies in excess of 3 carats are very rare and this pair of stones is quite exceptional. Photograph courtesy of Patrick Aldridge, Gemcut SA, Geneva.

Today a considerable range of synthetic ruby is grown by a whole variety of modern laboratory techniques. Many of these gems require intricate and sophisticated testing before their man-made origin can be proved. In the case of virtually inclusion-free synthetic rubies, for example, the present-day gemmologist has to employ infra-red, visual and ultra-violet spectroscopy.

Principal Gemstones that Can Simulate Rubies

SPINEL: can look very like ruby and was regarded as a variety of it for many years. Synthetic red spinels have been made and although generally uncommon a number of fine large synthetic crystals have been exported from the USSR in recent years.

GARNET: a number of the red varieties can simulate ruby. The rare true pyrope garnet is the closest in colour.

GARNET-TOPPED DOUBLETS: were made in the nineteenth century from a thin layer of natural garnet on to which coloured glass was fused and then cut. These are a convincing ruby simulant and can be made in many colours.

TOURMALINE: the rubellite variety very rarely reaches a true rich ruby colour.

DIAMOND: extremely rare in this colour, but there is one case recounted by the famous nineteenth-century jeweller Edwin Streeter of a fine red diamond being found in a parcel of rubies.

BERYL: no true red variety was known until the 1960s. A small deposit was then discovered in the Thomas and Wah Wah Mountain ranges in Utah, USA. Red beryl is sometimes known as Bixbite.

TOPAZ: very rare natural red topaz is occasionally found in Ouro Preto, Minas Gerais, Brazil.

QUARTZ: rock crystal which has been heated and plunged into red dye has been used to simulate ruby.

ZIRCON: bright-red zircons are found in the gem gravels of the Anakie sapphire fields of Australia and in the gravels of Nigeria.

CHRYSOBERYL, VARIETY ALEXANDRITE: in artificial light can occasionally be ruby red.

GLASS: some ruby-red varieties of glass are produced.

SAPPHIRE

The name of this gemstone is derived from its blue colour, and it has featured throughout history as one of the principal gemstones. In the ancient world the word sapphire was also applied to several other gems, and there are today very few surviving examples of true sapphire that can be dated earlier than the Greco–Roman period.

Sapphire alone is now exclusively used for the blue gem-quality variety of the mineral corundum. With the colour as a prefix the word is also applied to all other gem varieties of corundum excluding the red (or ruby), as, for example, yellow sapphire, green sapphire, purple sapphire, and so on.

From the medieval period until the late nineteenth century the name sapphire was applied only to the blue gem-quality variety of corundum, while all other gem varieties of corundum were given names reflecting those stones that they closely resembled. Thus the yellow sapphire was known as the "oriental topaz", the purple sapphire as the "oriental amethyst", and so on.

The star sapphire is a variety which is always cut *en cabochon* or dome-shaped. When it is viewed with a single bright light source, a six-ray (or more rarely a twelve-ray) star can be seen, which will move across the surface of the stone as it is rotated.

A range of rough and cut rubies and sapphires, showing a small sample of the possible natural colour range. These are from assorted localities. Photograph courtesy of C. Cavey.

CHEMICAL COMPOSITION: Aluminium Oxide with a small percentage of the colouring elements Iron and Titanium. Coloured sapphires have varying colouring elements, including Chromium.

COLOURS: all colours other than red, sometimes parti-coloured. Also colour-change varieties from green to red and blue to mauve when viewed in daylight and incandescent light.

CRYSTAL SYSTEM: trigonal.

HABIT: commonly elongated, barrel-shaped crystals with a hexagonal outline. There are many additional forms, ranging from flat to elongated prisms, to extremely thin, flat, tabular plates, frequently found as water-worn pebbles.

HARDNESS: 9. There should be no difference, in theory, between the hardness of sapphire and that of ruby. The crystals of ruby frequently incorporate lamellar twinning, however, and this means that in practice rubies are easier to damage than many sapphires.

CUT: faceted in a wide range of styles, cut *en cabochon* (sometimes producing star stones), engraved and carved in a great variety of ways.

History

The sapphire has been revered as one of the principal "precious stones" (a term no longer favoured) for many thousands of years and these stones are found in quantity in nearly all the crown jewels of Europe. There are examples of the sapphire being employed in the breastplate of the Jewish High Priest, and Moses is said to have engraved the Ten Commandments on a sapphire using a diamond as a carving tool, although it is now generally accepted that the stone in question was lapis-lazuli, which was widely used in ancient Egypt both prior to and later than Moses' time. Lapis-lazuli is in any case a comparatively soft stone and can be engraved quite easily.

Since the Middle Ages the sapphire has been worn by the bishops, cardinals and popes of the Roman Catholic Church. Not only did the colour represent the heavens, but the stone itself was believed to be "holy" and to bestow the virtues of being "pacific, amiable, pious and devout" upon the wearer.

At one time the mere presence of a sapphire was supposed to kill any venomous creature which came close to the wearer by exuding heavenly rays. The stone was employed in a number of medicines to ease

A plaque carved from a single piece of rock crystal, of Ancient Mexican origin. Photograph courtesy of C. Cavey.

inflammation in the eyes, to quell bleeding and to relieve and drain painful ulcers. Even the famous seventeenth-century chemist Robert Boyle refused to reject the use of this and other gemstones in the treatment of pain and disease.

Apart from its medicinal uses, either through direct application to ulcers and so on, or as a powder ingested in potions, the sapphire was also worn for a number of amuletic purposes. In some countries it was worn to suppress wicked and impure thoughts (a possible reason for its use in ecclesiastical rings), to pacify enemies and to give freedom from enchantment and captivity.

Other beliefs associated with the sapphire are so numerous it would be impossible to catalogue them all here, but a few examples are enough to illustrate their range. Sapphires were valued very highly by the necromancers of the Middle Ages and Renaissance, who used them to help interpret strange oracles and visions. They were also employed by some to protect them from poisons and by others to influence the powers of spirits.

The star sapphire was regarded by many as the most potent of amulets, and the three arms of the star have been interpreted as representing faith, hope and destiny. This gem was known at the court of the sixteenth-century Austro-Hungarian Emperor Rudolf II, where it was called the "stone of victory". The famous nineteenth-century explorer Sir Richard Burton carried a large star sapphire with him on all his

A portrait of George Gisze, by Hans Holbein the Younger, beautifully illustrating the dress and minimal jewellery worn by wealthy merchants of this period. 16th century. Photograph courtesy of C. Cavey.

travels and managed to explore vast areas of Africa and the Middle East without coming to serious harm. He would show the stone to a few selected natives, probably in order to make them fear its power should they intend to deceive him.

The sapphire is still used in some schools of crystal healing for the calming and balancing of the mind.

Sources

Sri Lanka produces more fine-quality sapphires than any other locality. The gem deposits of Ratnapura have yielded quantities of gems for over 2000 years and today the bulk of large fine sapphires are still mined from there. This deposit offers a colour range unequalled elsewhere and is the principal source of yellow, colourless, pink and purple sapphires of a large size. The general mine run of blue sapphires here is of a rather pale blue colour. Rarely, intense orange stones with flashes of red are discovered, and these are highly prized for their religious virtues by the local people, who call them *padparadsha*, a name derived from the word *padmaraga* meaning "lotus-coloured".

A number of fine stones have come from the deposits of the Mogok Stone Tract of Upper Burma, although this locality is more famous for rubies. The material at its best is a deep rich blue colour, darker than most of the material from Sri Lanka.

The best sapphires from mines in Thailand are also generally a dark blue, and a large number of them are dark blue-black to black in colour. Black and brownish golden star material is also found here and quantities of green, yellow, and mixtures of these two colours are common. Most of this material is found in stream gravels as water-worn pebbles. The deep dull colours are mainly due to high percentages of iron being present in the stone.

Kashmir produces a small quantity of milky pale-blue sapphire from a very inaccccessible deposit some

The sapphire mines of Poi Hi Krong, Palin, Cambodia. Photograph courtesy of E.A. Jobbins.

15,000 feet up in the north-western Himalayas. When heat-treated these stones achieve an extraordinary brilliant milky-blue colour. Sapphires from this locality are regarded in the gem trade as the finest, most desirable, and consequently most valuable of all.

Some very fine blue sapphires have also been found in the mines at Pailin in Cambodia, although mining there has been very erratic in recent years because of political unrest.

In Yogo Gulch, Montana, a quantity of sapphire is produced. The bulk of the blue material is small and in flat crystals. It rarely produces gems in excess of 1

Opposite: A superb ruby and diamond art deco ring and bracelet, accompanied by a 19th-century emerald and diamond brooch. Among the loose stones there is a fine ruby cabochon, and a string of very rare faceted diamond beads. Photograph courtesy of Patrick Aldridge, Gemcut SA, Geneva.

A sapphire cameo engraved with a portrait of George V (King of England 1910–36). Made in India to commemorate his Jubilee in 1935. 7 Carats. Photograph courtesy of C. Cavey.

carat. These are of a metallic blue and frequently colour-change from blue to purple. A wide range of pale-coloured sapphire in many shades is found at this locality.

In South America, the Cauca area of Colombia produces a range of coloured sapphire, and the Matto Grosso area of Brazil yields a small quantity.

An extraordinary range of colours is mined in the Umba River Valley area of Tanzania in Africa, where large fine star stones are occasionally found, and sizeable colour-change star stones are also discovered. Zimbabwe produces a small range of fancy coloured and blue sapphires, while Nigeria offers large quantities of dark-blue material, similar to the stones from Thailand, and has a deposit of green sapphire which turns red in incandescent light. Black star sapphires of a large size come from Guinea as a by-product of gold and diamond extraction from alluvial deposits.

Sapphires are also found in many other parts of the world, but not currently in quantities of any commercial significance.

Treatment of Natural Sapphires

Many natural sapphires are being heat-treated by a number of different methods to improve and sometimes completely change their colour, both from light to dark and from dark to light. In the case of yellow stones, colours are being artificially produced by a variety of radiation sources, and sometimes the resultant colour is unstable and will fade over a period of time in bright daylight. Glass-infilling of fissures and cracks is now used in an attempt to improve the appearance of inferior stones. Heat treatment and diffusion of colourants into the surface of stones only is also to be found.

Synthetic Sapphires

These have been made since the late nineteenth century. The colouring elements of sapphire are less easy to calculate than those of ruby. Early attempts to produce synthetics that provided convincing imitations were a failure. Synthetic sapphires were being made in commercial quantities by the 1920s, but most of these were of lower quality than equivalent synthetic rubies. With the development of electronic controls and timers in the 1950s it became possible to produce better-quality and more convincing sapphires by the Verneuil method.

This method is now used to grow cheap synthetic sapphire in some quantity, not only to simulate sapphires themselves but in a complete colour range to imitate other gemstones. Nearly all colours are common except green. A synthetic sapphire coloured by vanadium is produced to simulate the rare colour-change chrysoberyl, alexandrite. Early examples changed from a convincing green to red, while the bulk of stones made today turn from blue to mauve.

Today a whole range of sophisticated synthetic

sapphires are grown which require careful examination and refined laboratory testing techniques. Curious doublets (stones made of two layers of the same or different materials), consisting of a crown, or top of the stone, made of a thin layer of natural

A cabochon-cut natural colour-change (blue/violet) sapphire from Sri Lanka, surrounded by natural pearls. Stones of this kind were used for bishops' and cardinals' rings in the middle ages and Renaissance. Photograph courtesy of C. Cavey.

sapphire cemented on to a pavilion, or base, of verneuil synthetic sapphire, are made in Thailand.

Principal Gemstones that Can Simulate Sapphires

SPINEL: dark blue varieties can look very like sapphire, and other colours can easily be mistaken on first sight for fancy sapphires. Synthetic spinel is made in a full range of colours, all of which can also initially be mistaken for varieties of sapphire.
GARNET: can simulate fancy pink and orange sapphires.
GARNET-TOPPED DOUBLETS: made in the nineteenth century from a thin layer of natural garnet on to which coloured glass was fused and then cut. These are a convincing simulant and can be made in many colours.
BERYLS: aquamarines come rarely in a colour to simulate sapphire. Other beryls could be mistaken for certain fancy sapphires.
TOURMALINE: because of its wide colour variety can simulate a number of sapphire colours, although it does not usually come in any colour similar to the fine blue of the best gems.
DIAMONDS: rare in this colour, but a range of blue diamonds in varying intensity is known.

A range of natural and synthetic star stones. The top two stones are natural, the bottom two synthetic, and the black stone is a star diopside. Photograph courtesy of E.A. Jobbins.

TOPAZ: in its various colours could be mistaken for sapphire.
TANZANITE: a material that was only discovered in the 1960s, the only other natural gemstone that commonly occurs in a colour range similar to natural blue sapphire.
CHRYSOBERYL: yellow chrysoberyls can be mistaken for yellow sapphire, and the alexandrite variety may occasionally be ruby-red in artificial light.
GLASS: a number of varieties of coloured glass are produced to imitate sapphires.
IOLITE (Cordierite): is sometimes used as a sapphire simulant.

EMERALD

The name emerald is now exclusively used to describe the chromium-coloured green variety of the mineral beryl, although some African sources produce material predominantly coloured by vanadium. Emeralds can be found in extraordinarily bright and vivid transparent shades of green, but most stones come in mixed shades and intensities of colour and may sometimes be totally opaque. A few examples of fine green emeralds dating from the Roman period are still in existence today. However, most of these stones are internally fractured and translucent rather than transparent.

The emerald ranks next in commercial value to the ruby, and fine examples can cost more than the highest-quality colourless diamonds.

CHEMICAL COMPOSITION: Beryllium Aluminium Silicate with sufficient Chromic Oxide (and sometimes some Vanadium Oxide) to colour the stone green. However, not all varieties of green beryl are classified as emeralds.
COLOURS: green, in various intensities.

A large slice from a Russian emerald crystal which has been polished and engraved with a Bacchanalian scene. It was engraved with the number 176 on the reverse. It was certainly made for a gem collection and there is no evidence it was ever mounted in jewellery. Photograph courtesy of C. Cavey.

CRYSTAL SYSTEM: hexagonal.
HABIT: prismatic, elongated and flattened crystals.
HARDNESS: 7.5–8.0.
CUT: most commonly cut in such a way as to minimize loss of materials, stones are nonetheless shaped in all styles, carved in relief and in the round, and engraved in cameo and intaglio.

History

The Latin and Greek term *smaragdus*, from which our word is derived, is usually translated as "emerald", although it was widely used in the ancient world to describe a multitude of green gem materials. It is therefore wiser to assume that not every mention of the emerald in translated texts refers to the modern gemstone.

Wealthy Roman citizens wore true emeralds as jewellery, and examples of pierced, simply-polished crystals strung on necklaces can be seen in many European museums. The Emperor Claudius had garments made for him that were smothered in jewels set with emeralds and sardonyx.

The Romans also used the gems for a variety of other purposes. An emerald would be placed on a table, so that by gazing at it the owner might relax and soothe the eyes. It was even believed that a serpent unfortunate enough to look up at the stone would be immediately blinded. When engraved with a "bird harpe and under its feet a sea lamprey" an emerald could be employed as a pacifier, to dispel bad dreams and to reduce stupidity. If placed under the tongue it was said to give the user visions of future events. The Emperor Nero, watched the gladiatorial combats that were popular during his reign through a "viewing glass" made from an extremely large transparent emerald, and during his time green gems were even referred to as "Neromanus". Whether Nero's glass was a true emerald is a debatable point, although it is interesting to note that the colour red when seen through such a stone appears a dull grey, so the full horrors of the Roman arena would have been muted by its use.

Emeralds had religious connotations too. They were one of the gemstones used in the breastplate and the finger ring of the Jewish High Priest. In some versions

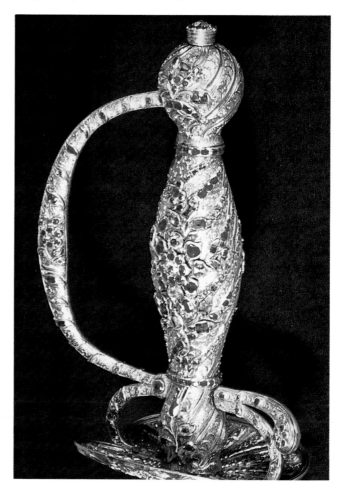

A gold sword hilt, set with ruby, emerald and diamond, with blade, known as the Gainsborough Sword. It was common practice to award these elaborate swords to distinguish generals and officials. Circa 1760. Photograph courtesy of E.A. Jobbins.

An emerald and diamond necklace with detachable clips, circa 1940. Made by Cartier. Photograph courtesy of Jacobs Lack Archutowski, Bond Street Antique Centre, 124 New Bond Street, London .

of the Arthurian legends, the Holy Grail, the bowl supposedly used by Christ at the Last Supper, is described as being carved from a single crystal of emerald by the hands of God and his angels. It is worth noting, however, that one of the most desirable objects a rich Roman could own was a cup made from a purple-banded variety of fluorite, a mineral found in large transparent green pieces which makes a very convincing emerald simulant. It is therefore possible that the Grail was a vessel made of green fluorite.

With the discovery of the Americas in the late fifteenth century and the subsequent conquest of Peru and Colombia, large quantities of superb emeralds became available for the first time. A number of these stones were set in jewels during the Renaissance period, and surviving examples can be seen in the jewellery galleries of the world's principal museums.

A belief in the supernatural properties of the emerald survived for many centuries. To break or lose one used to be regarded as an ill omen. During the coronation of the English King George III, an emerald fell from his crown, and this was later interpreted as a portent of the madness that was to afflict him. Emeralds were also supposed to preserve the chastity of women and to shatter into many pieces should the hapless wearer cease to be pure. However, this must have been an unreliable indicator, since emeralds tend to be brittle and most have a number of cracks, inclusions and fissures which make them easy to break even during the course of normal wear.

Powder made from ground emeralds has been used in a variety of medicines from the dawn of antiquity. Indeed, stones of low quality are still ground into a fine dust and used as an ingredient by present-day apothecaries in India and China.

Sources

In the ancient world emeralds were obtained from the Cleopatra Emerald Mines, in the area of Zabara near the Red Sea in Egypt. A few stones have been mined from this source recently, but they are of poor quality.

The oldest European source is probably the mine at Habachtal, near Salzburg in Austria. A few fine gems have been produced at this locality over the last 600 years, but the bulk of the material is a rather pale colour and included. Emeralds have also been extracted from the Ural Mountains area of the USSR for many centuries, and extremely large crystals over 10,000 carats have occasionally been discovered there. These are commonly pale, but transparent areas of intense colour can be found within some of the stones and produce very fine gems.

Among the countries of Asia, Afghanistan is a legendary source of fine emeralds and a few Afghan stones of truly exceptional colour still find their way on to the international gem market from time to time. In recent years neighbouring Pakistan has become a major producer of small fine-coloured emeralds, although much of the material is too dark and included to cut into larger gemstones.

A group of six Columbian emerald crystal specimens and one superb ruby from Burma. Photograph courtesy of B.S. Lloyd of Gregory, Bottley & Lloyd.

The principal home of fine large emeralds is Colombia, which sometimes produces flawless crystals of superb colour in excess of 1,000 carats. The chief sources are the Muzo Mine, the Chivor Mine, the Burbar Mine and the Gachala Mine. A strange star-shaped emerald occurs in Colombia and is known as a "Trapiche" emerald. Brazilian emerald production has come to rival that of Colombia and fine Brazilian stones compare favourably with the best Colombian material. There are a number of mining areas, mainly in the states of Minas Gerais, Bahía and Goiás.

Africa is now a major emerald-producer and supplies a significant part of the world's markets. The countries currently mining stones in commercial quantities include Ghana, the Malagasy Republic,

Mozambique, Nigeria, South Africa, Tanzania, Zambia and Zimbabwe, while the finest coloured African emeralds so far have come from the Sandawana Emerald Mines of Zimbabwe.

In addition, emeralds are mined in India, the USA (particularly North Carolina), Norway and Australia.

Treatment of Emeralds

It has been customary for many hundreds of years to soak emeralds in fine oils in order to hide the cracks and fissures usually present in most of these gems. So well established has the practice become that it is generally accepted by the world's dealers, although treatment with coloured oil is not approved. Recently, emeralds impregnated with resin in a vacuum have come on to the market. This process produces a similar effect to oiling but is virtually permanent.

Synthetic Emeralds

True synthetic emeralds have only been manufactured in the last seventy years. There are two distinct types, those grown from a flux melt and those grown hydrothermally in an autoclave. A number of manufacturers are now making very convincing synthetic emeralds, which can be extremely hard to detect if they are free from inclusions, although the chief gem-testing laboratories are equipped to identify them. The following synthetic types have been commercially available: Zerfass, Chatham, Gilson, Regency, Byron, Inamori, Lechleitner, Lennix, Russian and Seiko. Lechleitner also produces synthetic emerald-coated colourless beryls, and a sandwich of colourless beryl alternating with layers of synthetic emerald.

Principal Gemstones that Can Simulate Emeralds

GARNET: the chrome andradite garnet, demantoid, and the chrome grossular garnet, tsavorite and hydrogrossular varieties, can all be confused with emeralds.

GARNET-TOPPED DOUBLETS: these were made in

A range of fine rubies (ring and earrings), five good-quality natural emeralds, and two natural blue, two natural yellow, and one very fine colourless diamond. Photograph courtesy of Patrick Aldridge, Gemcut SA, Geneva.

the nineteenth century by fusing coloured glass on to a thin layer of natural garnet and then cutting. They are a convincing simulant and can be made in many colours.

OTHER BERYLS: green beryls that do not strictly qualify as emeralds can nonetheless be mistaken for them. Colourless beryls, synthetic spinel and quartz doublets with a green gelatine cement layer have been marketed as "Soude Emeralds".

TOURMALINE: when green tourmaline was first discovered in Brazil it was taken for emerald. Chrome tourmaline can be very similar in colour to fine emeralds.

CHRYSOBERYL: bright emerald-green chrysoberyl can be mistaken for emeralds, as can alexandrites of a fine bright-green colour when viewed in daylight.

JADEITE: can occur in a nearly transparent emerald green.

PERIDOT: can occur in a shade of pale emerald green, but only very rarely.

FLUORITE: can easily be confused with emerald, but is much softer.

AVENTURINE QUARTZ: can easily be mistaken for emerald in beads or in carvings.

STAINED GREEN CHALCEDONY: is cut in small sizes and used as a cheap emerald substitute.

GLASS: has been used to simulate emerald for many years and can be quite convincing. Some stones with many inclusions look like lower-quality emeralds.

YTTRIUM ALUMINIUM GARNET (YAG): a green variety of this synthetic material was produced in the 1970s and can be mistaken for emerald in small sizes.

A number of rare gemstones can also be confused with emeralds, and the reader is advised to refer to specialized works on gemmology for further information about these.

AQUAMARINE AND OTHER BERYLS

The name aquamarine comes from two Latin words (*aqua* meaning water and *mare* meaning sea), alluding to the usual blue-green colour in which this gemstone is found. The mineral beryl is sometimes mined in gigantic opaque crystals (up to 60 feet in length) to extract the rare element beryllium. Beryls, if pure, are colourless, and various colouring elements produce a wide range of gemstones (see also emerald).

Historically the name beryl seems to have been applied to the blue, blue-green and green (not emerald green) varieties. It is quite possible that there were no other colours of beryl available to the ancient world, or that they were known by another name.

CHEMICAL COMPOSITION: Beryllium Aluminium Silicate (see also emerald). The various colours are due to small quantities of colouring oxides.

COLOURS: Nearly all colours are known. The majority of all gem beryls are found in pale shades of colour. The following names have been applied to beryls of different colours. Green beryl coloured by chromium or vanadium oxide: Emerald. Blue and blue-green beryl coloured by iron oxide: Aquamarine. Yellow and golden beryl coloured by iron oxide: Heliodor. Mauve or pink or orange beryl coloured by manganese oxide: Morganite. Colourless beryl: Goshenite. Red beryl coloured by manganese: Bixbite (these are very rare and were only discovered within the last twenty-five years). Green (other than emerald) and brown beryls do not have specific names.

CRYSTAL SYSTEM: hexagonal.

HABIT: prismatic, elongated and flattened crystals occur. Sometimes found as etched masses, and as water-worn pebbles.

HARDNESS: 7.5–8.0.

CUT: a wide variety of styles; manx are faceted, or

A colour range of cut beryls including emerald, aquamarine, morganite and heliodor, with a crystal of aquamarine and emerald in the background. Photograph courtesy of E.A. Jobbins.

A fine crystal of green beryl carved with an otter sliding down an ice flow into a wave base, carved from rock crystal. Carved by G. Dreher. Photograph courtesy of P.V. Keane.

A superb pair of dolphins, carved from one large crystal of aquamarine, and mounted on to a carved rock crystal wave base. Carved by G. Dreher. Photograph courtesy of P.V. Keane.

cabochon cut, although cat's-eyes and six-ray star stones are known. This gem is frequently carved in relief and in the round, and engraved in cameo and intaglio.

History

Beryl (particularly aquamarine) has been used as a talisman, and for a range of medicinal purposes since the Middle Ages. Beryls were worn to bring victory in legal disputes and in battle, where the wearer was supposedly unconquerable. Other properties of this gem were to make the wearer more friendly, quicken the intellect and cure laziness. To this gem has been attributed the property of re-awakening faded love in long-married couples. Aquamarine has been utilized in the relief of pain, ailments of the mouth (including toothache), throat, stomach, liver, for swollen glands and diseases of the eyes. Sometimes even spectacle lenses were made from large pieces of a pale colour.

The pale aquamarine was regarded in the Renais-sance period as superior to the gemstone rock crystal when it was used for "crystal gazing" (cut as a crystal ball). The pale blue colour was thought to be symbolical of the colour of the moon, and this gem would therefore be subject to its influences. These spheres were thought to be at the height of their powers when the moon was full and its gravity at its strongest. As the aquamarine is named after sea water it is not so surprising that people thought it would be similarly affected by the pull of the moon's gravity. There are many stories of the crystal gazer advising kings and princes accurately of future events, but a number of these no doubt allude to spheres of rock crystal rather than the much rarer aquamarine. Of all the transparent spheres I have seen, none made of beryl date back before the beginning of the twentieth century.

Sources

Beryl is found throughout the world, but commercial gem-quality deposits are limited to a few major producers. Brazil is the major source of many gem varieties of beryl. In the state of Minas Gerais, flawless gem-quality crystals of aquamarine have been found in excess of 3 × 1 feet. Morganite occurs in large crystals, pale-yellow heliodors are not uncommon and quantities of green beryl are found. Curious bi-coloured crystals occur, part aquamarine and part morganite. Crystals of four colours are known. These have formed when the crystal growth has stopped and then restarted after a change in the various colouring elements. Nearly all the largest examples of gem beryls known are from Brazilian localities.

The USA produces a wide range of gem beryls. The stone is mined in the states of California, Maine, North Carolina, Colorado, Connecticut, South Dakota, New Hampshire, Idaho, and Utah. California produced the original morganite, which was named earlier this century by George F. Kunz after J. Pierpoint Morgan. Goshenite is named after Goshen, Massachusetts, where it was first recorded.

The USSR produces a range of aquamarine and some of the finest heliodors, from the Ural Mountains area.

In Asia, quantities of aquamarine come from Sri Lanka and from Kashmir in the north of India and Madras in the south. In the last twenty years Pakistan has also produced a number of aquamarines and morganites. Most of this material is finely crystallized, but the bulk is not of facetable quality.

The Malagasy Republic of Africa produces a wide range of fine-quality beryls and some exceptionally dark-coloured aquamarines. Some of the finest coloured morganite also comes from this locality and heliodors of fine colour are occasionally found. Nigeria has in recent years produced large quantities of aquamarines, found in numerous pegmatite veins. Zimbabwe, Kenya, Zambia, Namibia and Mozambique all produce gem-quality beryls.

Finally, Australia has recently produced aquamarine from Mount Surprise, in North Queensland.

A very finely executed female portrait engraved on an aquamarine and set in a contemporary gold and enamelled mount. Circa 1650. Photograph courtesy of C. Cavey.

colourless if they are overheated. Morganites are often orange when they are mined and with mild heating most of them change to pink. Beryls can be coloured deep blue by irradiation, but all the stones so far examined faded to nearly colourless when exposed for about six months to bright sunlight. The colour of some fine golden heliodors is enhanced by irradiation and heat treatment.

Synthetic Beryls

Are not produced on a commercial basis as the process is expensive. It costs no more to produce a synthetic emerald than any other colour in a beryl. So all current production centres on emerald.

Treatment of Beryls

All varieties of beryl (other than emerald) are subject to heat treatment. A number of green beryls will change colour under mild heat treatment to an equivalent shade of blue and therefore become aquamarines. Green beryl will sometimes turn to heliodor under heat treatment. All beryls will become

Principal Gemstones that Can Simulate Beryls

The colours and properties of beryls are so similar to a number of other gem species that simulants are too innumerable to list here. All prospective beryls should be subjected to standard gemmological testing methods to confirm their identity.

CHRYSOBERYL

The name chrysoberyl was derived from the golden-coloured variety of this gemstone. "Chrysos" means golden and beryl refers to the beryllium content in this gemstone. Chrysoberyl has only been used to describe this group of gemstones in the last 150 years.

The principal historical gemstone in this group is the cat's-eye. This is a cabochon-cut stone which has fine parallel fibrous inclusions of the mineral rutile. The stone has the appearance of a real cat's eye, and this optical effect is referred to by gemmologists as chatoyancy. The name cat's-eye used singly and without qualification is an exclusive term to describe this variety of chrysoberyl. (Note, however, that many other gem varieties produce stones with strong cat's-eye effects.) An alternative name for the cat's-eye variety of chrysoberyl is cymophane, which was derived from the Greek. This means "wave-like" and describes the appearance of the rough material more accurately than the finished product.

The regular-faceted chrysoberyl has been referred to historically by a number of names, but the most common of these is chrysolite (originally oriental chrysolite). This name was used to describe a bright pale-yellow variety of the gemstone, which was imported and set in jewellery in quantity by Portuguese goldsmiths during the eighteenth and nineteenth centuries. The same word is sometimes employed today by dealers in antique jewellery when describing these pieces, but this is confusing, as the name chrysolite is normally used to denote a bright yellow-green variety of the mineral peridot.

One of the most commercially desirable varieties of chrysoberyl is the gemstone known as alexandrite, which gained its name after its reported discovery in nineteenth-century Russia on the birthday of Tsar Alexander II. This variety of chrysoberyl is coloured by a small quantity of chromic oxide which gives rise to a curious optical phenomenon. The stones usually appear to be a green colour in daylight, and change colour to brown, red, purple or violet (depending upon their colour intensity and locality) when they are viewed in candle light or under the kind of normal incandescent lighting provided by a standard light bulb. The name alexandrite is all the more appropriate, as some of the Russian stones change from green to red, both of which are the colours of the Imperial Russian flag.

CHEMICAL COMPOSITION: Beryllium Aluminum Oxide with various oxides of Iron and Chromium to colour.

COLOURS: rarely colourless, more usually shades of yellow, golden, brown, grey and black. Green in various hues, sometimes nearly intense emerald-green. Red and mauve by incandescent light and very rarely red in daylight. Alexandrites have to change colour from green to red, mauve, or brown to qualify for this name.

CRYSTAL SYSTEM: orthorhombic.

HABIT: most frequently found as water-worn pebbles but when in crystal, most commonly pseudo-hexagonal triple twins, and rarely as single crystals.

HARDNESS: 8.5.

CUT: commonly cabochon, faceted, seldom found in sufficient size to carve. Rarely engraved.

A group of cut and rough chrysoberyls (including alexandrite) and spinels, showing their principal colours. Photograph courtesy of E.A. Jobbins.

History

The name chrysoberyl as used in the ancient world is unlikely to refer to our modern gemstone. It is far more likely that this name was applied to a bright yellow-green chrysoprase, and that the gemstone was not known as a distinct species by its modern name until the eighteenth century.

Cat's-eyes were known in the East for many thousands of years, but were so highly valued locally that there is little evidence of many finding their way to the West before the medieval period. These stones were, and still are, regarded in the East as the most potent of amulets against the effects of the evil eye.

Today, in India, cat's-eyes are prescribed in crystal healing and in medicines to cure a range of ailments. They are used by certain schools as a powerful tool for the treatment of all forms of cancer.

Alexandrites are a recent discovery and therefore have little history, although fine examples command a very high price on the world markets. Cat's-eye alexandrites are not uncommon, and have been used for healing.

A group of faceted chrysoberyls (excluding alexandrite) showing how they can vary in colour and brilliance (colourless stones are very rare). Photograph courtesy of E.A. Jobbins.

Sources

Chrysoberyls in a wide range of colours and forms have been found in the gem gravels of Sri Lanka for thousands of years. When alexandrite was discovered in a Russian mine it was thought to be exclusive to that site. It was not long after this discovery, however, that a similar colour-change chrysoberyl was found in the Sri Lankan gem gravels. Most Russian alexandrite is different from Sri Lankan, in that the Russian stones tend to be a light to deep blue-green in daylight and change to a reddish violet and frequently to a pure purple. Sri Lankan alexandrites normally change from a wide range of greens to brown, reddish brown, or red.

The Russian mines no longer produce large quantities of alexandrite, although some is still coming on to the market. In recent years Zimbabwe, Brazil and India have all produced alex andrites with a fine colour change. Burma produces a few alexandrites, but is notable for some strange colour-change green chrysoberyls that turn blue, and for a range of pale and colourless stones.

The yellow and green varieties of chrysoberyl (which can sometimes cut cat's-eyes) are also mined in Madagascar, Zimbabwe, Mozambique, Japan, Australia, Brazil, and in a number of states in the USA.

A fine yellow-golden-brown chrysoberyl (21 carats), set in a high-quality gold and platinum mount, which is enamelled in white and red. Russian, circa 1900. Photograph courtesy of C. Cavey.

Treatment of Chrysoberyls

Chrysoberyl is not usually treated in its cat's-eye and faceted forms. Alexandrites are frequently included and cracked; these are commonly oiled and more recently resin-impregnated to improve the outward appearance of the stone.

Synthetic Chrysoberyls

The only variety of chrysoberyl that has been manufactured in commercial quantities is the alexandrite. These are normally grown by a flux melt method and contain inclusions which would normally identify their origin. Flawless specimens can be identified by experienced gem-testing laboratories with complex modern testing techniques.

Principal Gemstones that Can Simulate Chrysoberyls

Regular-faceted chrysoberyls can be simulated by natural and synthetic sapphires, topazes, tourmalines, grossular garnets, pastes, and a whole range of uncommon gem materials.

CAT'S-EYES: most commonly simulated by a similar-looking quartz variety, but a number of others exist. Those most similar in appearance are fibrolite, apatite, diopside and kornerupine.

ALEXANDRITE: commonly simulated by colour-change synthetic sapphires, the bulk of which change in colour from blue to violet. A few were manufactured in the 1930s which change from a more convincing green to violet. A green to red colour-change synthetic stone is manufactured in quantity.

NATURAL SAPPHIRE: occurs only rarely with a green to red colour-change, as do a small range of rather strange African garnets. A number of gemstones exhibit a colour-change phenomenon and are commonly referred to as "alexandrite-like", although this can and does cause considerable confusion. True, fine-quality alexandrites with a good colour change are not common in excess of 2 carats.

TOPAZ

The name topaz seems likely to be derived from the island of Topazion (now, probably, the island of Zeberget) in the Red Sea. This name was used to describe the gemstone peridot before the medieval period, and the gemstone which we now know as topaz appears not to have had an ancient name. The name could also come from the Sanskrit word alluding to "fire", which implies that the gemstone accepted as topaz in the ancient world varied from country to country.

In a number of countries the name of topaz is incorrectly applied to certain varieties of quartz. Sometimes these are referred to as topaz/quartz, and on occasion they are sold to the unsuspecting purchaser as a genuine topaz. This practice is misleading, as there is a considerable difference in the price of yellow and golden topaz and yellow and golden quartz. Today the name topaz is exclusively applied to only one mineral.

CHEMICAL COMPOSITION: Aluminium Fluorosilicate with Iron and Chromic Oxides to colour.

COLOURS: colourless, red, pink, orange, yellow, golden, brown, green (usually pale), blue, and rarely violet. Coloration in topaz can be caused by metallic oxides (orange, yellow, pink, red) or in some cases by natural and artificial irradiation (blue, golden, brown). These sometimes occur in natural bicolour crystals and cut gemstones, but are uncommon. True red topazes are the most commercially desirable but are very scarce. Topaz is often strongly dichroic (different colours in different directions), and carefully cut stones sometimes appear to have two colours.

CRYSTAL SYSTEM: orthorhombic.

HABIT: frequently found as pebbles, but sometimes comes in enormous crystals, up to a quarter of a ton.

HARDNESS: 8.

CUT: faceted and cabochon cut, engraved and carved.

History

The early history of true topaz is rather obscure.. It is one of the gemstones listed in the breastplate of the Jewish High Priest. The Roman Emperor Hadrian was reputed to have a ring set with an engraved topaz; but it is more likely that the author who described this ring and those who wrote many of the manuscripts on this subject were referring to the stone we now call peridot.

In the medieval period the topaz was regarded as having various powers and properties. When set in gold and worn round the neck, the stone was said to dispel bad dreams, remedy cowardice, calm anger, cure madness and brighten the wit of the wearer. It was used to heal dimness of vision, and there is one case recorded of a topaz curing the plague after a single touch. It was also believed to be an effective charm against witchcraft, and to lose its colour if in the presence of poison.

In the seventeenth century a large colourless topaz was misidentified as a diamond. This was surprisingly listed as the largest cut diamond ever recorded. The weight of the stone was over 1000 carats, and it was named the "Braganza diamond". It is curious to note that, had this stone been a diamond, it would

A woodcut published in 1483, illustrating the killing of a dragon to extract precious stones. Photograph courtesy of C. Cavey.

still be the largest ever recorded.

Topaz jewellery was extremely popular in the eighteenth century and it was used extensively in suites of jewels. Pink and yellow stones were frequently set with coloured foil backings in order to improve the colour and brilliance of shallow and pale gems.

The popularity of this gem faded in the late nineteenth century, but it is still highly regarded and frequently encountered in jewellery. In museums it is possible to find cut stones that are in excess of 20,000 carats.

Topaz is used for a number of purposes in modern crystal healing. The reader is referred to specialist works on this subject.

Sources

The most important gem-mining area for yellow, golden, and red topazes is that of the mines in Ouro Preto in the state of Minas Gerais, Brazil. Similar material is also found at a few localities in Pakistan.

Topaz which is colourless, brown and blue comes from many localities, in Europe, Burma, Sri Lanka, Australia, Africa, the USA and the USSR. Brazil and Russia have produced transparent gem-quality crystals in excess of a quarter of a ton.

Right: A fine pink and yellow topaz and diamond necklace. Italian, 18th century. Photograph courtesy of E.A. Jobbins.

Treatment of Topazes

The heating of yellow and golden topaz, which is coloured by iron and chromic oxides, usually produces pink and sometimes violet stones, but all these will lose their colour if they are overheated. This process has been in regular usage in the trade since its purported discovery by a Parisian jeweller in 1750. The heating of naturally irradiated brown stones sometimes turns them blue, and this knowledge has been employed to great effect in the last thirty years.

Colourless or very faintly coloured topaz is by far the most common variety of this gem species, and large quantities of such stones have in recent years been artifically irradiated to turn them a golden-brown colour. These are subsequently heated, which turns a proportion of them into various shades of blue (apparently a stable permanent colour), while the others revert to being colourless. When the initial irradiation is carried out, a number of sources are employed. The depth of colour is usually dependent upon the length of exposure and the radiation source.

A fine crystal and five faceted topazes (demonstrating their colour range) standing on a large cleft crystal of pale-blue topaz. Photograph courtesy of E.A. Jobbins.

to a few topazes coming on to the world markets that are still slightly radioactive. Most reputable gemmologists and testing laboratories can easily check these stones for any signs of radioactivity.

Synthetic Topazes

Topaz is not currently made synthetically in commercial quantities.

Principal Gemstones that Can Simulate Topazes

Some of this material can remain radioactive for nearly twelve months, so it is normally left in store to "cool down".

Concern has recently been expressed in the world's trade press about the possibility that some of these stones are still radioactive. Material treated in the West under strict regulations is almost certainly safe. Many sources of the rough material are in Third World countries, and poverty and greed has in some cases led

The principal natural gemstone that simulates yellow topaz is citrine, a variety of quartz. Sapphires and spinels, both natural and synthetic, can easily be mistaken for topaz. Aquamarine and blue topaz are often confused, and a number of tourmalines have a similar appearance. Garnet-topped doublets and paste can make very convincing simulants.

There is a very wide range of rare and unusual gemstones that can be mistaken for topazes.

SPINEL

The origin of the name spinel is not certain, but it is probable that the word is derived from the Latin word *spina* which has been translated as "thorn-like". Spinels are frequently found as sharp double-pyramid-shaped crystals (octahedra) and can be quite sharp at the points.

There is an entire group of minerals covered by the general name spinel, although the bulk of these are not gemstones and are therefore omitted from this work. The red gem spinels were for many years regarded as a variety of ruby, and the reader is referred to this section for additional information. There are several gemstones other than pure spinels in this

group, and these are normally referred to by their specific names, the most common of which are Gahnite, Gahnospinel and Ceylonite.

CHEMICAL COMPOSITION: Magnesium Aluminum Oxide, but many elements substitute for one another. Coloured by various metallic Oxides, usually of Iron, Titanium, Manganese and Chromium.

COLOURS: nearly colourless; red in various shades and intensities, sometimes rivalling the colour of the finest rubies; orange, green, blue (rarely intense cobalt blue), violet, grey, black and totally opaque black. Really bright colours are rare.

51

A gold button set with a number of uncut bright-red natural spinel crystals. Photograph courtesy of E.A. Jobbins.

CRYSTAL SYSTEM: cubic.
HABIT: commonly water-worn pebbles, but does occur in sharp octahedral crystals, which are sometimes flattened and twinned, producing macles (spinel twins).
HARDNESS: 8.
CUT: frequently faceted, and was used extensively in cabochons (sometimes cut as star stones). These stones have been carved as leaves and figures for decorating a wide range of religious objects. Spinels are very rare in large sizes.

History

Virtually all the principal large historical rubies to be found in the crown jewels and treasure houses of the world are fine examples of red spinels. Many are engraved with the names of their illustrious owners and have bloody and complex histories. The properties and beliefs associated with these red gems are the same as for rubies. The other colours of spinel have few beliefs associated with them, and it is quite probable that these were not actually fully identified as belonging to this group of gems until the middle of the last century.

Sources

The bulk of gem spinels of fine quality come from the mines of the Mogok Stone Tract in Upper Burma. A wide colour range of material is found in the Sri Lankan gem gravels, although the bulk of this material is a rather dull colour and the red stones rarely have the intensity of those from Burma. Afghanistan, Pakistan, and the USSR all produce gem-quality spinels, and they are found as a by-product of ruby and sapphire mining in Cambodia and Thailand. Nigeria produces blue Gahnite spinels as a by-product of tin-mining. There are many small deposits of spinels throughout the world, but few produce many stones of gem quality.

Treatment of Spinels

Included spinels are sometimes oiled and infilled with glass to hide cavities and cracks.

Synthetic Spinels

Since the 1930s a range of colourless and coloured spinels has been manufactured and marketed. When the colourless material came on to the market it caused a considerable scare, as it made a reasonably convincing diamond simulant when it was cut in small stones. These were made by the quick and cheap flame fusion process. Natural spinels have suffered consider-

A range of faceted natural spinels showing the commercially desirable colours. Photograph courtesy of E.A. Jobbins.

A selection of syntheic boules grown by the flame fusion method, and showing examples of synthetic spinels, rutile, rubies and sapphires. Photograph courtesy of E.A. Jobbins.

stones, and colourless stones have been cut as doublets with a green cement layer to make passable imitation emeralds.

In the 1960s a range of colours (including red) were grown by the expensive flux melt process. These can be hard to distinguish from natural spinels when they are of similar colours. Recent production in the USSR of large facetable red synthetic flux melt spinels is causing concern on the gem markets.

Principal Gemstones that Can Simulate Spinels

Spinels in their various colours can be mistaken for rubies and sapphires, but the bulk of gem spinel is of a dull colour and only a few gemstones are likely to be confused with these.

Red varieties of garnets can occur in a very similar colour to spinels and fine pyrope garnets have frequently been taken for these gems. aste and garnet-topped doublets make good imitation spinels.

ably from the stigma of being identified with the synthetic gems made as a cheap diamond substitute. This was because ignorant traders commonly referred to any diamond simulant by the name spinel. Due to this misunderstanding red spinels have yet to regain their popularity.

Synthetic spinels have been made in a wide range of colours (excluding red) as simulants of other gem-

TOURMALINE

The general name tourmaline is derived from the Singhalese word *turamali* which has been translated as meaning a stone of mixed colour. The word tourmaline is used to describe a varied group of minerals which all have similar chemical and optical properties. These can vary considerably even within the one gemstone, and this can cause complications for gemmologists when trying to identify them.

There are a number of varietal names given to the different coloured tourmalines, but in practice most of these are rarely used by the world's gem trade. The principal names used in the trade are given here as a general guide, and these usually relate to the colour of the stone.

The name elbaite originally applied to multicoloured tourmaline from the island of Elba, Italy, but the general chemical group of this type of tourmaline covers a whole range of colours and provides the bulk of gem material in a wide variety. Rubellite is a name

usually applied to all red-coloured tourmalines, indicolite is the name that was first applied to dark transparent blue-black tourmaline. These are now

A group of faceted tourmalines demonstrating the range of colours possible in this gemstone. Photograph courtesy of E.A. Jobbins.

heat-treated to lighten the colour, and a practice of calling all blue tourmalines by this name is not uncommon. Brown tourmaline is known as dravite. Schorl and uvite generally refer to opaque black tourmalines. Tourmalines exhibiting two colours in parallel are normally referred to as bicoloured, and stones that have a red central core and a different surrounding colour or colours are referred to as "water melon" tourmalines. The tourmalines that exhibit many colours in one stone are called multicoloured tourmalines. Chromic oxide coloured tourmaline is known as chrome tourmaline.

CHEMICAL COMPOSITION: a complex Boro-silicate, containing Sodium, Aluminium, Calcium, Lithium, Boron, Iron, Fluorine and Potassium. These vary considerably from stone to stone.
COLOURS: an enormous range. Sometimes as many as twelve separate colours can be seen in one stone.
CRYSTAL SYSTEM: trigonal.
HABIT: most commonly as long needle-like crystals, sometimes as inclusions in other gems, commonly in quartz, beryl and topaz. Also found as water-worn pebbles in gem gravels, and a wide range of crystal shapes.
HARDNESS: 7.5.
CUT: Faceted and cabochon stones are common. Sometimes cabochons exhibit a good cat's-eye affect. Stones may be carved in cameo, in intaglio, and in the round.

Tourmaline in matrix, when these are cut on a cross section they are referred to as water-melon tourmaline. Photograph courtesy of B.S. Lloyd of Gregory, Bottley & Lloyd.

A section through a large multi-coloured tourmaline crystal, showing why it is sometimes called "water-melon tourmaline", after the distribution of colour in the crystal, from Madagascar. Photograph courtesy of B.S. Lloyd of Gregory, Bottley & Lloyd.

History

Tourmalines have only been identified as a separate gem species for a matter of 200 years. The stones originally found in Brazil in the sixteenth century were mistaken for emerald and it was not until the eighteenth century that this error was corrected.

Although this gemstone has a brief history, it has been used in medicines and optical instruments since its discovery. Tourmaline possesses many curious properties, and some of these gems make very fine polarizing filters (the original polarizers were made of tourmaline slices mounted in gold tongs). The tourmaline's electrical properties (stones develop a strong charge when rubbed or compressed) are utilized in

A fine bi-colour tourmaline crystal, in its natural state, from Minas Gerias, Brazil. Photograph courtesy of B.S. Lloyd of Gregory, Bottley & Lloyd.

seismographic (earthquake) detection equipment. The electrical charge developed by these stones will attract dust and ash, in the same way that iron filings are attracted to a magnet. Modern crystal healers use tourmalines in meditation and for a wide range of curative purposes.

Sources

This gemstone is produced in many countries throughout the world. Several localities have yielded fine gem-quality crystals several feet in length. Large spectacular crystals are found in Brazil, in Maine and California, USA, and in Madagascar.

Many countries in Africa are now producing quantities of fine gem-quality tourmaline, and this is also found in several countries in Europe, Asia, and Australia. The reader is referred to specialist textbooks for detailed locality information.

Treatment of Tourmalines

Heat treatment is commonly used to lighten, change and improve the colour of the material. Irradiation is sometimes used in conjunction with heat treatment. Carved tourmalines are often resin-impregnated to reduce the chance of splitting or damage during the carving process.

Synthetic Tourmalines

Tourmaline has been made synthetically, but only in small quantities for scientific research projects.

Principal Gemstones that Can Simulate Tourmalines

There are many gemstones that can be mistaken for tourmaline.

GLASS IMITATIONS, DOUBLETS AND COMPOSITE PRODUCTS all provide material that could simulate tourmaline.

GARNET GROUP

The name garnet is applied to an entire group of minerals which all have a similar chemical grouping, but whose properties vary considerably from one type to another.

The word garnet is derived from the Latin *granatum*, which refers to the fruit pomegranate. This no doubt alludes to the common occurrence of garnets as bright-red spherical grains in rocks, looking like the seeds in this fruit. A number of varietal names are applied to the different members of this group and to commercially important sub-varieties within each group. I shall attempt here to outline some of the origins of names applied to the varieties of garnet.

The name pyrope is derived from the Greek word *pyra*, which is translated as "like a burning coal" and alludes to the bright (almost ruby) red colour of these stones. The name almandine is probably derived from its source in Alabanda, in Asia Minor. Almandines vary in colour from black to deep brown, red to purple and pale violet. The name spessartine is derived from the locality of this gem in Spessart, in north-west Bavaria, Germany. Spessartines are bright orange when pure, and become redder to dark red as their iron content increases. Rhodolite is a name applied to a rose-red variety of pyrope almandine garnet, and is derived from the Greek word *rhodon*, which alludes to its colour. Pyrandine is the name suggested by the late Basil Anderson for garnets consisting of part pyrope and part almandine garnet.

The name grossular was derived from the gooseberry-green colour of the first garnets of this type to be classified. Grossular garnets have now been found in a wide range of colours, although pure stones are colourless. Hessonite,

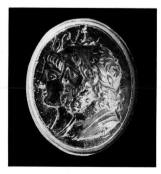

A finely engraved double portrait of Serapis and Isis, engraved on a hessonite garnet (jacinth). Circa 2nd century. The stone is set in a modern platinum and gold fob. Photograph courtesy of C. Cavey.

an orange grossular garnet, is named after the Greek word meaning "inferior", a reference to its lower hardness. Tsavorite (chrome grossular garnet) is named after its principal locality, Tsavo National Park in Kenya. The reader is warned of the dubious practice employed by some dealers and auction houses in describing these stones merely as "green garnets". This variety has only been widely available on the world market for twenty years, and is frequently sold to the unsuspecting customer in place of the more valuable andradite garnet, demantoid.

Hydrogrossular garnet is a massive compact variety of grossular garnet and comes in white, pink, brown, and green. A bright-green chrome-coloured variety is sometimes referred to as "Transvaal jade" after its principal location. A hydrogrossular garnet which is intermixed with the mineral idocrase is named californite, after its principal locality in the state of California, USA. Malaya garnet is a term derived from the Bantu word implying "of mixed parentage", as this garnet is a variable mixture of pyrope, almandine, spessartine and grossular.

Andradite is a name applied to a group of garnets, and is derived from the name of the mineralogist d'Andrade. This is sometimes called the "common garnet" as non-gem qualities are very frequently found in a variety of rocks. Normally it is a pale brown colour but it can vary considerably. Demantoid is a name derived from the "diamond-like" fire and appearance of this bright-green garnet, which is currently the most valuable and commercially desirable member of the garnet group. These stones, in sizes over 1 carat, can be comparable to or more valuable than emeralds of a similar quality. Yellow andradite garnets are referred to as "topazolites", from their colour. A jet-black variety of andradite is known by the name "melanite".

Uvarovite is named after the Russian Count Uvarov. This variety is usually a deep-green colour, but is hardly ever encountered as a gemstone.

CHEMICAL COMPOSITION: garnets are usually

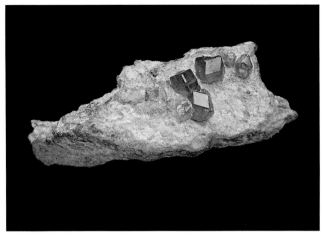

Three Mogul Indian jewelled thumb rings. The left-hand ring is carved from a single garnet and has inlaid diamonds set in gold. The central ring is carved from nephrite jade and is set with carved rubies and emeralds. The right-hand ring is made of gold and is inlaid with rubies, emeralds and enamel. 17th–18th century. Photograph courtesy of E.A. Jobbins.

Demantoid garnet on asbestos from North Italy. Photograph courtesy of B.S. Lloyd of Gregory, Bottley & Lloyd.

named after the closest chemical group to which they belong. The principal names of the garnets and the varietal names are as follows: pyrope: Magnesium Aluminium Silicate; almandine: Iron Aluminium Silicate; spessartine: Manganese Aluminium Silicate; grossular: Calcium Aluminium Silicate; andradite: Calcium Iron Silicate; uvarovite: Calcium Chromium Silicate.

COLOURS: nearly all colours are possible, but truly blue garnets are very rare. Colour-change garnets are known (blue to mauve and green to red are recorded).

CRYSTAL SYSTEM: cubic.

HABIT: in crystals, commonly twelve and twenty-four faced, and frequently in variations of these. As pebbles and grains in rocks.

HARDNESS: 6.5–7.5.

CUT: commonly cabochon-cut and faceted, engraved and carved.

History

The garnet in one of its forms was probably set in the breastplate of the Jewish High Priest. According to Eastern legends, a garnet was suspended in the ark by Noah to disperse light. Garnets were used in ancient Egypt, but they were either not very popular or they were only available in very limited quantities. By the time of classical Greece and Rome, red carbuncle

(cabochon garnets) and orange hessonite (hyacinth or jacinth) were freely used in jewellery, and were often engraved in cameo for decorative purposes, and intaglio for use as seal stones.

Many of the beliefs associated with rubies were also attached to garnets, which were once regarded merely as varieties of the same stone. The term carbuncle is usually used in literature to describe a cabochon garnet, which is sometimes hollowed on the underside to lighten the colour of the stone.

Garnets were employed in the medieval period for curing heart palpitations and diseases of the lungs, for dissolving tartar and for resisting melancholy.

Male and female garnets were thought to exist, and were both used as small sacred windows through which light would pass. In common with other red

A selection of garnets, rough and cut, showing their colour range and form. Photograph courtesy of E.A. Jobbins.

stones, garnets were thought to warm the heart, help circulation and assist in suppressing bleeding, and were used in curing diseases of the blood. They were frequently employed as the eyes of idols and statues, and were even used by the natives as bullets on the Kashmir frontier in the nineteenth century in the belief that they would be more effective than lead!

Garnets have been used to ward off evil spirits, and are still employed by apothecaries in India for use in a wide variety of treatments. Various forms of garnets are used in modern crystal healing.

Sources

Garnets are found worldwide, but a few important localities will be mentioned here.

Pyrope garnets are found mainly in Trebnitz in Czechoslovakia, and these have been used in many items of jewellery for over 500 years. Many pyropes are found in the kimberlite rocks when diamond is mined. True bright-red pyrope garnets are quite rare.

Almandine garnet is found worldwide, but India, Africa, Sri Lanka, Australia, America, and Europe all have important sources of this material.

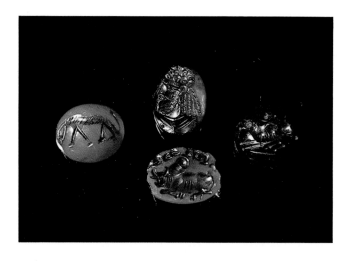

Group of Sassanian seals, three in chalcedonies and the top is an imperial portrait in garnet, circa 5th century. Photograph courtesy of C. Cavey.

Spessartine garnet in fine colours is found in Minas Gerais, Brazil, and a number of places in North America. The Broken Hill Mines of New South Wales, Australia, produce a deep orange-red spessartine garnet.

Grossular garnet was originally discovered in the

USSR, but is now found in many African countries, and in Sri Lanka (predominantly hessonite) and Burma. Tsavorite comes from Kenya and Quebec, Canada. Hydrogrossular garnet is mined commercially near Lake Jaco in Mexico, and in the north Transvaal, South Africa.

Andradite garnets are rare in gem quality. Demantoid garnets come from the Ural Mountains in the USSR and from northern Italy.

The garnet group is complex and furnishes the gem kingdom with a wide variety of colours and types. The reader is referred to specialist texts for further information.

Treatment of Garnets

In the more valuable varieties some stones are resin-impregnated to hide cracks and inclusions.

Synthetic Garnets

No commercial production of synthetic garnets of compositions similar to natural garnets have been reported.

Principal Gemstones that Can Simulate Garnets

The principal gemstones to be commonly mistaken for red garnets are rubies and spinels. Garnet-topped doublets are frequently taken for solid garnets, and a dark-red synthetic ruby has been manufactured as a garnet simulant.

TOURMALINES, SPESSARTINE GARNET AND YELLOW TOPAZES: can be confused with hessonite garnets.

EMERALDS, TOURMALINES AND A NUMBER OF RARER GEMSTONES: can be confused with demantoid and tsarorite garnets.

JADE: hydrogrossular garnets can easily be mistaken for varieties of jade.

GLASS: makes convincing imitations of nearly all varieties of garnet.

TURQUOISE

The name turquoise was derived from a word meaning "Turkish". This alluded to its supply route from Iran through Turkey, which was the only source of this gemstone for European markets.

CHEMICAL COMPOSITION: Copper Aluminium Phosphate.
COLOURS: Blue, green, yellowish, white, and grey. Sometimes this material is cut with veins of the brown iron mineral limonite running through the turquoise.
CRYSTAL SYSTEM: Triclinic.
HABIT: Normally nodules and veins; very rarely crystalline.
HARDNESS: 2.5–6. Best gem material 5–6.
CUT: Cabochon, carved and engraved.

History

The use of turquoise for jewellery and in amulets dates back to the dawn of civilization. The ancient Egyptians utilized this gemstone extensively, but material was in limited supply and costly. They made many imitation turquoise objects and carvings, by first cutting the required object out of a very soft steatite (talc), then covering it in a glaze (in this instance powdered blue glass mixed with a liquid), and finally firing in a furnace to produce a turquoise-coloured object. Many of these imitations still survive today.

The turquoise has been known by its current name since the medieval period. It has not been confused with many other natural stones and has a set of supposed properties that apply uniquely to it. The principal virtue by far (chronicled first in the thirteenth century) was the ability to save the wearer from injury when falling. The stone was supposed to break the wearer's fall, and by itself breaking, protect the wearer from harm. The value of such a stone at that time could not be underestimated. Travel on horseback in dangerous conditions would invariably result in a few occasions when the rider would lose his grip and fall.

Many Turkish soldiers had bridles set with this stone in the belief that it would protect a very hot horse from the considerable ill effects of drinking cold water. The turquoise was famous for use as a horse amulet, and the sky-like colour of the stone no doubt played a considerable part in this belief. The horse was employed in solar symbolism and it was therefore quite natural to relate the sun (horse) with the sky (turquoise).

Turquoises have been said to lose or change colour when danger is near or the wearer or owner of the stone is unwell or close to death. The stones would apparently regain their brilliance and colour when transferred to a healthy new owner.

The ability of a turquoise to tell the time of day was unique to this stone. It would be suspended from a cord and, when held between the thumb and index finger near a glass, any slight movement was said to

A sample range of the mineral turquoise. At the rear the rough material is from Cornwall, England. The engraved and gold inlaid stones are 19th-century. Persian good luck charms. The scarab and tiger amulet are Ancient Egyptian (the scarab is in a 19th-century gold mount). Photograph courtesy of C. Cavey.

59

result in the stone chiming the hour. To protect against evil, the turquoise was employed by the Persians as a mirror for looking at the image of the new moon. Good luck charms were often carved in this stone and then infilled with gold leaf. The ancient Pre-Columbian cultures of the Americas and the native Americans of the north and Mexico all have complex beliefs, myths and lore relating to this gemstone.

The reader is referred to other works for additional information on turquoise history and lore.

Sources

Turquoise is mined today in a number of localities, and is still available from the ancient mines at Nishapur in Iran. It is mined in quantity in mainland China, Tibet, Egypt, the USSR, Mexico, and a number of localities in the USA.

Treatment of Turquoise

This gem material has been treated by wax impregnation for many thousands of years. This process is easily carried out due to the very porous nature of this gemstone. A great quantity of material is also steeped in dye prior to waxing in an attempt to improve the colour of inferior material.

In the last thirty years new processes have been developed to produce resin-bonded turquoise, which

A group of Chinese and Iranian cut and uncut turquoises. Photograph courtesy of E.A. Jobbins.

remains stable over a number of years. Untreated turquoises frequently discolour during normal wear; fine blue stones will often turn green, due to chemical reaction with oils and acids in the skin and the surrounding atmosphere.

The bulk of turquoise mined is of very porous nature, and is frequently full of cavities. This material is therefore unusable without some form of treatment. Resin impregnation in a vacuum stabilizes the material, and if the resin is mixed with finely powdered turquoise, this will fill most of the cavities and cracks. Artificial blocks of resin-bonded powdered turquoise are marketed under the name of "reconstructed turquoise".

Composite carvings made of many pea-sized pieces of turquoise and small pyrite grains are cemented together in a similar manner to "reconstructed turquoise". These are currently under production in Hong Kong and Taiwan.

The non-destructive testing of turquoise can be very difficult, and on some occasions virtually impossible. This factor has had a major impact on the value and world market price of this gemstone in the last twenty years.

Synthetic Turquoise

A material described as synthetic turquoise was first manufactured by Pierre Gilson of Paris. This did not truly synthesize the gemstone, although further attempts have proved nearer to the formula and structure of the natural material. A synthetic turquoise complete with natural-looking "limonite" veins has now been on the market for some time. Synthetic products of these types frequently require laboratory examination before identification can be confirmed.

Principal Gemstones that Can Simulate Turquoise

Although a few minerals occur in nature that can be confused with turquoise, all of these are uncommon, and most are rarer than turquoise itself.
CHRYSOCOLLA-COLOURED CHALCEDONIES: make the closest naturally-coloured turquoise simulant (stained chalcedonies are also used).

THE FELDSPAR, AMAZONITE: comes in colours similar to turquoise but invariably has structural patterning.
VARISCITE: is found in various shades of green and can be mistaken for green turquoise.
GLASS IMITATIONS: of turquoise can sometimes be very convincing, particularly in small sizes.

There are a number of stained minerals such as howlite and magnesite which are sold as turquoise simulants. Natural fossil mammoth ivory coloured in the ground by blue phosphate of iron (vivianite) produces a convincing simulant known as odontolite.

OPAL

The name opal is probably derived from the Sanskrit word *upala*, which has been translated as meaning "a precious stone". The Greek derivative of this, the word *opallios* literally develops the name one stage further and has been translated as meaning "to see a change in colour".

There are many forms of opal, the majority of which are not used as gem materials. Only a few varieties have the characteristic play of colour that is generally associated with this gemstone, and these are referred to as "precious opal". Other varieties of opal that do not exhibit a colour play are generally referred to as "common opal", although the orange fire opals which have no colour play are often regarded as a form of precious opal.

Opal in its many forms can take on the external shape of other minerals, animals, and plant remains that have dissolved away and left a "mould" in the surrounding rock into which the opal permeates and solidifies. These are generally referred to by the term "pseudomorph", a word used to describe any mineral material that takes on the form (and sometimes the structure) of another material. Examples of opals that have replaced wood, ancient bones, and fruits are exhibited in a number of the world's major museums.

A full breakdown of all the names applied to the wide range of common opals is beyond the scope of this publication (see the bibliographical section for specialist works on this subject).

Precious opals have a wide range of names applied to them, and these generally refer to the colour play of the material. The names white, grey and semi-black, and black opal, all refer to the basic body colour of the stone (ignoring the colour play). There are other terms, such as "water opal", which refer to the transparent water-like body of such stones. The names

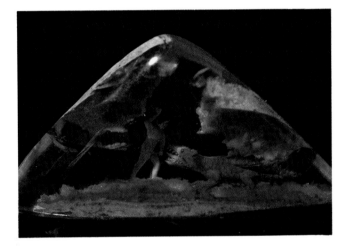

A triangular cabochon-cut Mexican fire opal, engraved on the rear with Siegfried slaying the dragon. Circa 1920. Photograph courtesy of C. Cavey.

matrix and boulder opal refer to a group of these gems which are cut in such a way as to retain some part of the surrounding rock in which they were found. Sometimes a variety is cut that is mainly ironstone matrix, which is permeated by many fine seams of brilliantly coloured opal, occasionally producing extraordinary scenic effects.

The colour play of opal has an entire range of terminology. The most commercially desirable of these gems are known as harlequin black opals. This is in reference to their black background colour, and the colour play which is divided into quilt-like segments (like the costume of the fabled harlequin). The best of these will have a preponderance of red and orange flashes of colour, with other colours balancing this effect.

The term "flame opal" refers to stones that have a colour play that appears to resemble a flickering flame.

The term "flash opal" is used for stones which have little colour play when viewed in some directions, and then give a flash of colours when viewed in others. "Peacock opal" is a term used to describe the blue-green, almost iridescent colours of this form of opal, which have a similar appearance to the feathers in a peacock's tail. "Pinfire" is used to describe opal that has a colour play divided into tiny pinhead segments.

There are a number of additional terms used to describe the infinitely variable colour play in precious opals. These generally refer to other structures, objects and forms, which most closely resemble the appearance of the gem in question.

CHEMICAL COMPOSITION: Silica with a variable percentage of water. The water content can be as high as 20 per cent, but is usually a little under 10 per cent in the majority of precious opals.
COLOURS: all colours and an infinitely variable colour play.
CRYSTAL SYSTEM: none. Opal is a variable amorphous mass.
HABIT: in nodules, boulders, seams, veins, sometimes replacing other structures, organic and inorganic.
HARDNESS: 5.5–6.5.
CUT: most commonly as cabochons in many shapes. Occasionally faceted, particularly in the case of fire opals. Sometimes carved and engraved in cameo and intaglio.

History

There is some degree of doubt that the stone known as opal in the ancient Roman world was, in fact, our modern gemstone. There are a number of references to this gem by various classical authors, but all specify that these gems were found in locations that do not produce opals today. The description of these stones however, does conform closely to that of the modern opal.

The opal in the classical world was regarded as possessing all the properties and virtues of all the other gemstones. This was primarily due to the fact that properties were linked with colour, and since the opal exhibited all colours it was therefore assumed to share the virtues of all the gemstones. Mark Anthony is said to have gone to extraordinary lengths, and finally committed homicide, in order to obtain a large highly-valued opal from the Roman senator Nonius.

True opal was certainly known in the Renaissance

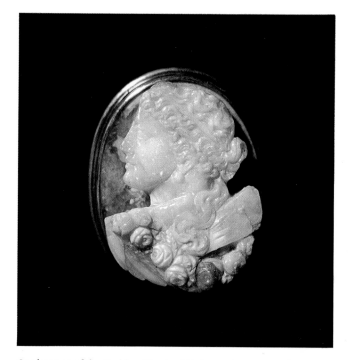

Opal cameo of the Goddess Psyche. Photograph courtesy of C. Cavey.

period, and a number of examples survive. The bulk of this material was white opal with a colour play, although fire opal with a colour play was also known. This gemstone was used for treating and relieving diseases of the eyes, as it was supposedly a variety of the "opthalmius" (eye stone). The stone was employed by magicians, who were said to use it to become invisible, but few details of this procedure survive.

A number of superstitions exist connected with the opal, not least of all that they bring bad luck to all persons except those born in the month of October. Several reasons may account for this belief, including the very fragile and unstable nature of the gem itself. The origins of such beliefs no doubt derived from the gem's name and its association with the eyes. Careless translation or misreading gave rise in some quarters to a belief that this stone attracted the evil eye, and hence was the unluckiest of stones.

One story tells of a Turkish Sultan spreading the rumour that these stones were unlucky, in the hope that he could purchase them cheaply when the price had fallen. Apparently the tale took such a grip that the Sultan himself started to believe it and would no longer buy the very opals he had coveted. The most damaging chapter in the history of the opal's properties came in the nineteenth century with the publication of a novel by Sir Walter Scott entitled *Anne of Geierstein*. In this book opals were linked with bad luck, and people subsequently began to believe that

Carved iridescent matrix opal representing on this side a "golden pheasant", and on the reverse is an elaborate doorway. This carving was exhibited at the World's Fair in Chicago, in 1954. I think the subject is intended to be the mythical phoenix rising from the ashes, and the doorway on the reverse represents the gateway through death to the afterlife. Carved by Alfred L. Pocock prior to 1954. Photograph courtesy of Mrs W. Bottley.

the story was in fact true.

Opals were very rare gemstones in the early part of the nineteenth century and only became available in quantity towards the end of the century. Even today, the belief that opal is unlucky still persists among a large percentage of the world's population. Certainly nearly all the dealers in this gemstone have tales of horror to tell, but these usually only relate to the breaking of stones and hardly ever to any inherent ominous attribute possessed by this gemstone.

Sources

The localities of common opal are numerous, and therefore only precious opal will be dealt with here. The oldest known source of opals is the deposit in what was once Hungary and is now part of Czechoslovakia. The bulk of this material is white opal with a varied colour play, and more rarely fire opals with a brilliant red-green fire.

A few stones were mined in Honduras in the early part of the nineteenth century but few are seen today. In the 1850s the wonderfully rich deposits of Australia were discovered, and it was at the turn of the century that the first black opals were found at the mining district of Lightning Ridge. Opals are found at a number of localities in Australia, and one of the most commercially important opal-mining areas in the world today is Coober Pedy in South Australia.

Deposits of fire opal were discovered at the beginning of this century in Mexico, and these still produce quantities of fine gem material today. Much of this material is very unstable and is liable to craze and even disintegrate within six months of mining. Brazil produces a wide range of high-quality white opal from its northern states, and the white opal production from these mines nearly rivals that of Australia.

Opal is found in the states of Idaho and Nevada in the USA, and some of this material occasionally filters on to the market. An extremely unstable black opal from Indonesia has been on the market in the last fifteen years, but nearly all these stones have crazed.

Treatment of Opals

This gemstone is sometimes unstable due to its variable water content. Newly-mined material can frequently crack up, sometimes on its surface (crazing) and sometimes so thoroughly that it will disintegrate entirely. Opals that have been subject to heating and forms of shock will easily break and crack. The practice of oiling these stones has been used for a long time. This will usually hide cracks that surface in the stones, but will dry out after a period of a few weeks. The impregnation of opals with hard-setting resins in a vacuum is now commonplace, and the reader is warned to be very careful of stones treated in this way; they are very deceptive, and the commercial value of the stone is greatly reduced by cracking and crazing.

Thin layers of opal are cut and cemented on to backs of poorer quality opal, stained black chalcedony, "black onyx", and black glass. These are known as opal doublets. When a clear transparent protective layer (usually rock crystal or glass) is cemented on to the top of these doublets, they are known as opal triplets.

Synthetic Opals

True synthetic opal was first produced in quantity by the French chemist Pierre Gilson. These have been available on the market for over twenty years. A number of companies produce types of synthetic opal today, and many of these can be very difficult to detect. Imitation matrix opal cameos are produced using a layer of highly-coloured synthetic opal cemented on to a background of natural ironstone matrix (in which natural opal is found).

A seated rodent carved in precious opal with small cabochon ruby eyes, carved by Alfred L. Pocock in 1955. This carving is in a similar style to the work he carried out for the Royal Family between 1905 and 1914, under commissions from Fabergé's London shop. Photograph courtesy of Mrs W. Bottley.

Principal Gemstones that Can Simulate Opals

A wide range of plastic imitation opals are now produced and all of these can be very deceptive. A type of glass with bright iridescent coloured spangles was produced in the USA. This was marketed under the name of "slocum stone". It can be deceptive to the inexperienced eye. Other varieties of glass have been made, containing crushed foil and various inclusions to simulate a number of the varieties of opal.

The natural colour play in some types of labradorite feldspar, and in some moonstones, can lead them to be confused with opal.

MILKY QUARTZ: can sometimes be mistaken for poor-quality opal.

LUMICHELLA (FIRE MARBLE): can have an iridescent opal-like appearance.

COMMON OPAL: can look like many of the variegated, translucent and opaque gem materials.

An iridescent type of chalcedony known in the trade as "fire agate": can be mistaken for opal.

QUARTZ

The general name quartz is applied to a large number of gem materials which all share the same chemical make-up and similar physical properties. This group of gem materials provides the largest and most diverse range of colour and form that occurs in hard gem materials. The varieties of quartz are found worldwide and are the most commonly available of all the gem species.

There are two basic types of quartz gem. The first group consists of the visibly crystalline types such as rock crystal, amethyst, citrine, and so on, and the second group is comprised of microscopic crystalline aggregates which come in an enormous range of colours and patterning and are all either translucent or opaque. A few examples of this type of quartz are chalcedony, agate, onyx, jasper and carnelian (sometimes named cornelian). There are a number of non-gem varieties of quartz: quartzite rock and many sandstones are mostly composed of this mineral.

The origin of the various names applied to the varieties of quartz is very complex, so the reader is referred to specific works on quartz for further information. The names of a few of the varieties of quartz are quoted here as examples. Rock crystal was named after the Greek word *krystallos*. The Greeks believed this variety of quartz was ice that had been frozen for so long that it would no longer melt. Amethyst and citrine are named after their respective colours. Carnelian is derived from the Latin word *carnis* and alludes to the blood-red colour of a small number of these stones. Prase is named after the Greek word *prason* which alludes to its leek-green coloration. And so on and so forth.

CHEMICAL COMPOSITION: Silicon Dioxide commonly referred to as silica, with small quantities of

A block of smoky quartz undergoing preliminary shaping by the carver, G. Dreher. After this stage a range of microscopic tools is used to engrave the fine details in the carving. Photograph courtesy of G. Dreher.

other elements to colour.

COLOURS: the transparent varieties of quartz are referred to by their respective names. Colourless quartz is rock crystal; yellow or golden or light-brown quartz is citrine; dark-brown to smoky brownish-black is smoky quartz (in Scotland this is called Cairngorm after the montain range in which it is found); black quartz is morion; pinkish/lilac/dark-mauve to purple quartz is amethyst. Material that is part amethyst and part citrine is sometimes referred to as "ametrine" or "trystine"; pink and peach colours, frequently slightly cloudy, are rose quartz (this sometimes produces star stones); green quartz is prasiolite. Milky, sometimes almost opalescent (opal-like) material is called milky quartz.

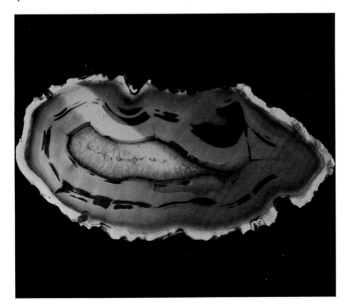

An unusual natural multi-coloured agate slice. Minas Gerais, Brazil. Photograph courtesy of C. Cavey.

Other varieties of transparent quartz which have been coloured by inclusions of other minerals are sometimes given specific names. Quartz with distinct included fibrous crystals of golden rutile is sometimes referred to as rutilated quartz or "sagenite". Quartz containing included crystals of tourmaline is referred to as tourmalinated quartz. One blue-coloured variety is coloured by finely intermixed crystals of the mineral dumortierite, and is known as dumortierite quartz; another is coloured a powder blue by masses of

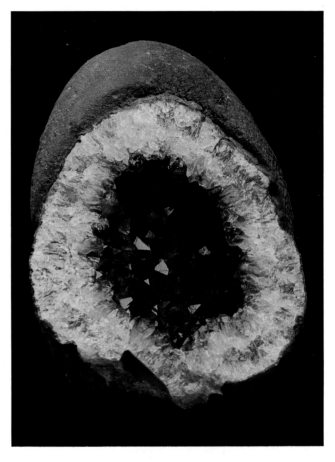

A round geode of amethyst crystals on a bed of agate. Minas Gerais, Brazil. Photograph courtesy of C. Cavey.

included blue rutile crystals. Gold occurs commonly in a quartz matrix. This is cut and used in jewellery, and is referred to as "goldquartz".

Many local names are applied to transparent varieties of quartz in the areas where they are found and are too numerous to list here.

Generally the common name of chalcedony is applied to all translucent varieties of quartz. All opaque varieties of quartz come under the general name of jasper. The name chalcedony is also applied, with the colour of the stones as a prefix, to a wide range of

A superbly carved smoky quartz seated polar bear, in full movement, by G. Dreher. Photograph courtesy of G. Dreher.

colours (natural and artificial). Red or orange chalcedony is usually referred to as carnelian (or cornelian). Brown chalcedony is sometimes referred to as sard. Black chalcedony is commonly, but incorrectly, referred to as onyx.

The name agate used without a prefix is generally applied to all banded varieties of chalcedony, and when pieces are cut from agate boulders which have only straight bands, this material is correctly referred to as onyx. White and brown and white and orange combinations of colour are referred to as sardonyx. A black variety with a thin blueish-white layer on the top is sometimes given the name "niccolo". Those varieties of agate referred to as moss agates are chalcedonies with inclusions of various metallic oxides which form moss-like patterns and coloration in the stones. A variety of moss agate known as "mocha stone" is usually composed of a pale cream or yellow background with black tree-like dendrites flowing just beneath the surface of the stone. There is a rare irridescent variety from Arizona and Mexico which is called "fire agate" and has an almost "opal"-like play of colour.

Plasma is a name used for dense-green varieties of chalcedony, while chrysoprase is a name exclusively applied to the bright-green variety of chalcedony coloured by the oxide of nickel. The name prase is used to describe green chalcedonies in general. The material called by this name by the Greeks and Romans now appears to be a rare type of natural chrome-coloured chalcedony. The only commercially significant occurrence of this material today is in Zimbabwe

Opposite: *Fossilized wood, showing an extraordinarily bright colour range. Photograph courtesy of B.S. Lloyd of Gregory, Bottley & Lloyd.*

where it is named "Mtorolite" after its locality.

There is a range of fine grained quartz (quartzite) coloured by inclusions; and the name aventurine is used to describe a variety coloured by tiny enclosed mica platelets. The bulk of this material is green in colour, but brown, orange and blue varieties are known. A fine brilliant turquoise-blue-coloured chalcedony occurs in Arizona. This is coloured by microscopic intermixed particles of the copper mineral chrysocolla, and is referred to as chrysocolla quartz.

The name heliotrope (and in some countries, blood-

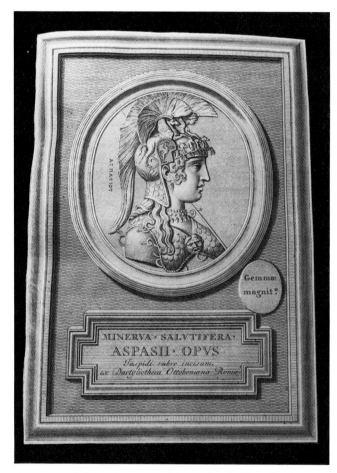

An engraved plate of a signed red jasper classical intaglio representing the goddess Minerva. 1724. Photograph courtesy of C. Cavey.

stone) is used to describe the green chalcedony or jasper which has red spots. Flint is a blackish-blue impure variety of chalcedony rarely used as a gem. Chert is an impure variety of flint and would normally be classed as a chalcedony. Chalcedonies vary widely and varieties are made up of a considerable range of replaced material.

Quartz commonly replaces organic and crystalline materials which have dissolved away in the ground, including the wood of ancient trees, many millions of years old, and dinosaur bone, muds, silts and a variety of minerals, sometimes taking on their appearance and minute details of their original structure. This furnishes an enormous range of gem material.
CRYSTAL SYSTEM: trigonal.
HABIT: frequently as hexagonal prisms with a double rhombohedral termination. As layers, crystalline and crypto-crystalline aggregates and pebbles, and so on.
HARDNESS: 7.
CUT: is cut and used in an infinite variety of ways.

History

Quartz gems have been used since the dawn of time, and have been employed by virtually all civilizations. The names of several varieties are mentioned in holy texts throughout the world. In the Bible, quartz gems made up the bulk of the stones in the breastplate of the Jewish High Priest. A number of the varieties of quartz were employed as seal stones by the great ancient civilizations of Egypt, Assyria, Babylon, Persia, Greece and Rome. Many properties, beliefs, and superstitions were associated with these gemstones and

A group of portrait intaglios executed in a number of varieties of quartz; these date from the 16th century to the 19th century. The portrait (bottom centre) is a contemporary rendition of Edward VI (King of England 1547–1553). Photograph courtesy of C. Cavey.

A cippus of Horus, made of stone and placed as a boundary stone on a property to protect it from the evil eye. 4th century B.C. Photograph courtesy of C. Cavey.

the nineteenth century, when the development of the natural sciences discredited earlier beliefs. There has recently been a considerable revival in the interest in rock crystal for use in foretelling future events, for healing and meditation. The centre of this renewed interest has been in the United States of America, but it has now spread throughout Europe and Africa. A number of books devoted to the use of rock crystal for innumerable mystic and other purposes have been published in the last twenty years, and the reader is advised to consult these for more details.

Agates, carnelians, onyxs, and other chalcedonies and jaspers all have various supposed properties. Some are birthstones, others are used for warding off the evil eye, stopping haemorrhage, and relieving diseases of the eyes and blood.

Sources

Varieties of quartz occur worldwide, but a few special localities are listed here.

Amethyst is produced in fine large stones from various states in Brazil, and from Uruguay. The principal European source is from the Russian mines in Siberia. Some of the most attractive crystalline specimens of this gemstone are found in the Vera Cruz area of Mexico. Most citrine is heat-treated amethyst so the localities for this gem are the same as those for amethyst.

it would be impossible to give comprehensive details here. The reader is referred to the final chapter of this book for references which will enable further study. A few examples of beliefs associated with quartz are quoted here to whet the appetite.

Amethyst has been worn for many thousands of years for its supposed property of instilling a sober and serious mind in the wearer. It was even believed that this gem would prevent wearers from becoming intoxicated when they consumed quantities of alcohol. It became the symbolical gemstone set in the rings of the Bishops and Archbishops of the Protestant Church.

Rock crystal has been cut as "crystal balls" for use by mystics to tell fortunes and predict future events since the time of ancient Greece in Europe, and was similarly employed in the ancient Chinese culture. The use of these spheres seems to have reached its zenith in the Middle Ages in Europe and to have tailed off towards

A group of "mocha stones" (dendritic agates) from Hindustan in India. In the 19th century these were highly valued, and the most desirable were the varieties which bore a resemblance to religious scenes. The stone on the left (9 o'clock) was thought to portray the "burning bush" which Moses encountered on Mount Sinai. Photograph courtesy of C. Cavey.

An orange-red carnelian vase, with small white chalcedony patches carved as branches and flowers. Chinese, 18th century. Photograph courtesy of E.A. Jobbins.

A group of three pictorial jaspers, and one green scenic chrysocolla from India. The box is English, circa 1750, and is set with panels of Egyptian jasper. The other picture jaspers are modern and come from Oregon, U.S.A. Photograph courtesy of C. Cavey.

Natural carnelian is noted as occurring principally in India. Chrysoprase is mined from two major sources: the old mines in Silesia, and the Aboriginal homelands in Australia. Fine natural blue chalcedonies are found chiefly in Turkey and South Africa. The reader is referred to specialist books on quartz for more information.

Two cut examples of rose quartz showing pronounced "diasterism" (a star effect seen when the stone is held up to a point light source). Photograph courtesy of E.A. Jobbins.

Rock crystal occurs worldwide. Enormous pieces are found in Brazil, USA, the USSR, Switzerland and the Malagasy Republic, while the largest recorded flawless rock crystal sphere (weighing 108 lb) was cut from Burmese material. Japan is noted for producing a rare type of twinned crystal.

Smoky quartz is found worldwide but fine spectacular specimens occur in Brazil, the Malagasy Republic and Switzerland.

Agates also occur worldwide, although rare types are noted from certain localities, the dendritic mocha stones, for example, being found principally in the area of Hindustan in India. A fine range of agates is found in Brazil, the USA, Australia and various African countries.

Opposite: *A highly polished transparent citrine stylized cat, reminiscent of art deco designs, carved by G. Dreher. Photograph courtesy of G. Dreher.*

Treatment of Quartz

The treatment of quartz minerals is very complex and it would be impractical to mention all methods here. A few examples are listed in an attempt to illustrate the scope of this subject.

Irradiation is used to turn rock crystal brown and black, while subsequent heat treatment will turn the material back to colourless through a range of browns and yellows. Rock crystal is used as the base material of a doublet with a gelatine layer which can be any colour, and may be used to simulate a number of other gemstones.

Amethyst is heated to produce the bulk of yellow citrines; the deeper the amethyst, the deeper the resultant citrine colour. Occasionally during this process stones will turn green and these are then named prasiolites. Natural heating by geothermal means or by forest fire can occur, so it is impossible to say whether all these stones have been artifically treated. Rose

A fine crystal group of transparent quartz (rock crystal), from the Dauphiné, France. Photograph courtesy of B.S. Lloyd of Gregory, Bottley & Lloyd.

quartz is sometimes cut in cabochons and a blue mirror backing is cemented to these stones. This produces a deceptive imitation of star sapphire.

Chalcedonies and agates are stained a variety of colours by boiling them in various colouring agents. Large quantities of raw chalcedony are of a dull grey colour when mined. Carnelian, agate and onyx have been stained by a variety of methods since the ancient Egyptian period. A practice of dropping heated rock crystals into coloured dyes was employed in the nineteenth century. The stone would fracture and the colouring material would enter the cracks, apparently tinting the stone. This is known as crackled quartz (naturally cracked material similar to this is known as iris quartz).

Rough uncut rock crystal specimens are being coated with a microscopically thin layer of gold. This gives them a strange iridescent pale-blue colour.

Synthetic Quartz

This has been manufactured for a number of years for the electronics industry. It has only been commercially available on the gem markets for about thirty years. Rock crystal is the most commonly produced material, but a range of colours is also made. Fine amethyst and citrine are manufactured, together with some colours that are not known in nature. The most common of these is a rich bright-blue quartz coloured by cobalt oxide. It can be difficult to distinguish between natural and synthetic quartz. The chalcedonies and jaspers are not currently synthesized.

Principal Gemstones that Can Simulate Quartz

Quartz comes in so many varieties and forms it can be confused with an enormous range of gemstones. In general the quartz gems are the most commonly available and are consequently normally the lowest in value. This factor makes them prime simulators of other gemstones, rather than being simulated themselves.

SOFT FORMS OF CALCITES, MARBLES AND SERPENTINES: all make convincing simulants of varieties of quartz.

GLASSES: are manufactured to simulate nearly all the varieties of quartz, from transparent to opaque.

FELDSPAR GROUP

This group of minerals forms part of many of the day-to-day rocks that are used in building materials. The orthoclase feldspar is a main constituent of the rock granite. The name for this group of minerals is derived from the Swedish words *feldt spat*, which refers to the occurrence of the material in fields overlying granite, and from the German words for "spar for the fields", which has much the same connotations. The feldspars are a complex group of minerals and the bulk of them furnish little gem material. Only the principal gemstones from this group will be dealt with here, and the reader is referred to other works for more detailed information.

Feldspars, like garnets, frequently intermix, and the most familiar of these gem materials is probably moonstone (a variety of orthoclase feldspar). This is a mixture of two types of feldspar, and the alternate layers of each cause an optical effect commonly referred to as sheen. This effect varies from stone to stone but the most commercially desirable gems have a transparent pale-blueish background with a flash (sheen) of several colours. Moonstones are named after their resemblance to the full moon. Other gem orthoclase feldspars consist of colourless and yellow transparent gemstones.

Microcline feldspar provides the gem variety amazonite, which is usually a turquoise blue-green and is transluscent to opaque. The name amazonite is derived from the Amazon river basin where it was discovered in quantity. Sunstone is a bright-golden-orange spangled plagioclase feldspar, which is coloured by minute inclusions of the iron mineral goethite. The name is derived from the stone's similarity in appearance to the setting sun.

Labradorite is a variety of plagioclase feldspar that is famous for exhibiting an iridescent colour play when it is viewed at one particular angle. This material is named after the large deposits of this gem found in Labrador, Canada. Colourless yellow, orange and red stones are known.

A variety of albite feldspar known as peristerite can have a colour play similar to labradorite. It is far rarer than labradorite and can easily be mistaken for it.

CHEMICAL COMPOSITION: Aluminosilicates with varying combinations of Potassium, Sodium, Calcium, and occasionally Barium. Metallic oxides are normally the cause of coloration.
COLOURS: see above.
CRYSTAL SYSTEM: variable monoclinic and triclinic.
HABIT: as grains in rocks and as distinct crystals, sometimes of a large size. Gem-quality material is very scarce in relation to the immense quantity of feldspars in the earth's crust.
HARDNESS: 6.0–6.5.
CUT: cabochon, faceted, carved and engraved.

History

Amazonite was used in many items of jewellery and decoration by the ancient Egyptians, and a number of sacred scarabs were cut in this stone. Moonstones were used by the ancient Greek and Roman cultures and religions, particularly by those who worshiped the various deities associated with the moon. The moonstone was said to fix the volatile spirit of minerals, and to be a very potent gift between lovers. It was also employed to fortell the future, but to effect this process it was necessary to place the stone in the mouth when the moon was full.

Stories have been told of moonstones visibly changing in various ways during the respective quarters of the moon. These gems have been used by many cultures in various parts of the world. The value of these stones tend to fluctuate following the trends of fashion. In the nineteenth century, a work of fiction was written by a well-known author of the day named Wilkie Collins. This was titled *The Moonstone*, and interest in this gem increased with the popularity of the book. Surprisingly this book still generates interest in this gemstone.

Feldspars were for many years classified as varieties of other gemstones, so accurate identification of these in old books and manuscripts can prove to be quite difficult.

Sources

Feldspars occur worldwide, although gem varieties are seldom found in quantity except in a few confined localities.

The finest moonstones in the world come from the island of Sri Lanka. They are also found in India, Switzerland, the USA, Canada, Greenland, Madagascar (also a source of transparent orthoclase) and Burma.

Fine-quality amazonite is found in Brazil, Africa, the USA, Switzerland and a number of other sources.

Labradorite is mined in its iridescent form in Canada, Finland, and several localities in the USA. A "moonstone-like" labradorite is found in Madagascar. Transparent facetable material is found in several states in the USA, but most notably Oregon, also in Australia and Mexico.

Although feldspars provide an interesting range of gem material, only a few of these gemstones are regarded as of commercial significance. The reader is referred to additional works for further information.

Treatment of Feldspars

Some varieties of feldspar are resin-bonded to make them easier to work, and to strengthen planes of weakness.

Synthetic Feldspars

There are no currently produced synthetic feldspars which can be mistaken for natural gems, although some have been manufactured and sold on the amateur lapidary market in the USA.

Principal Gemstones that Can Simulate Feldspars

Transparent faceted feldspars can be confused with varieties of quartz and beryl. Moonstones are imitated by milky quartz, mother-of-pearl, satin spar (a variety of gypsum), glass and an unusual variety of synthetic spinel.

Certain types of matrix opal could be confused with labradorite. Lumachella (fire marble) which contains inclusions of ancient iridescent shells could occasionally be mistaken for labradorite.

Sunstones are commonly simulated by a material known as "goldstone". This is a coloured variety of man-made glass which has many fine microscopic inclusions of crystallized copper. Amazonite can sometimes be confused with aventurine quartz.

JADE

Jade is a name which is now used to describe two separate gemstones which possess different properties. This name was apparently derived in ancient China from the term *Yu*. In the American, Pre-Columbian cultures it was called *Egiada*. Carved jade was known in Europe primarily from Chinese sources, although small quantities of the gemstone were found and used (as far back as the Stone Age) for axe heads and cutting tools. Virtually all this material is the mineral which we know today as nephrite.

Jadeite (the other jade mineral) was known principally to the ancient Pre-Columbian civilizations, but was in limited use in Japan, Korea and Burma. Very few objects made of jadeite were known in Europe until the discovery of the Americas, during the six-teenth century. The term *egiada* (a Pre-Columbian name) which has been translated as "stone of the kidneys" (or stone of the loins) referred to the material which we now call jadeite. The term *Yu* was used by the Chinese to describe their ancient form of jade and meant "stone of the heavens", which is now called nephrite.

It was eventually found that the jade from the New World was different from the ancient Chinese material, and during the eighteenth century various mineralogists attempted to define the minerals which were to be called by the name jade and to devise a

An apple-green jadeite lobed bowl. Chinese, 18th century. Photograph courtesy of E.A. Jobbins.

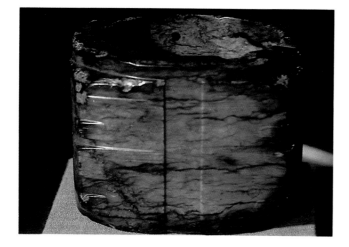

A nephrite jade "Tsung" which is artificially stained. Ancient Chinese, dating to approximately 1000 B.C. Photograph courtesy of E.A. Jobbins.

A carved nephrite jade chimera (a mythical beast, a composite of many other actual and fictional creatures). Chinese, 4th–6th century. The carver has skilfully employed the discoloured outer skin of the boulder to form the head and back of the animal. Photograph courtesy of E.A. Jobbins.

means of differentiating between the two stones. As a result the general name jade was to be applied to both minerals, nephrite and jadeite. Nephrite (derived from *lapis nephriticus* meaning "stone of the kidneys") was used for the ancient material from China and jadeite for the Pre-Columbian jades. This was most unfortunate, as no belief associated with benefit to the kidneys was linked to Chinese jade, and ironically the name jadeite was chosen for the true kidney stone.

The principal auction houses frequently catalogue nephrite as jade and jadeite as jadeite, which can confuse potential collectors.

CHEMICAL COMPOSITION: nephrite is the compact fibrous aggregate form of the minerals actinolite and tremolite. This material is a Calcium Magnesium Silicate with varying quantities of iron. Nephrite belongs to a mineral group known as the amphiboles. Jadeite is a Sodium Aluminium Silicate and is also fibrous, but less tough than nephrite. It belongs to another mineral group, known as the pyroxenes.

COLOURS: the Chinese have a complete set of names for various colours and types of jade and the reader is referred to specialist works for descriptions of these. Nephrite can be white, pale yellow, rarely intense "imperial" yellow, green in various shades (but never bright emerald green), grey, brown, black, sometimes stained and coloured by heating and impregnation with decaying organic compounds. All the material is normally transluscent to opaque. Ancient Chinese jades were frequently buried with their owners, and some were covered with a coating of the mercury mineral, cinnabar. These stones frequently exhibit a bright-pink or red coloration in porous areas. Nephrite will withstand high temperatures and after intense firing will become opaque with a light biscuit-coloured hue. Stones that were cinnabar-coated before firing usually developed pinkish areas. Fired nephrites of this type are known as "chicken-bone jades" in allusion to their coloration.

Jadeite occurs in a wide range of colours, and it is the bright almost transparent emerald-green variety of this type of jade that is commonly referred to as "imperial" jade. Fine pieces of this material are more costly than the equivalent qualities in emerald or other green gemstones (excluding only natural green diamonds). The colours in which jadeite occurs cover the entire spectrum, and some are more commercially desirable than others. The demand for good and fine green material is considerable. Lavender is the next most popular colour, although jadeite also comes in many shades of green, brown, orange, almost red, blue, blueish grey, white, colourless. Sometimes pieces show many colours within the one carving or cabochon. Jadeite, unlike nephrite, may also occur in virtually transparent pieces. It is quite easy to read newsprint through a fine stone, when it is placed in contact with it. Jadeite is most commonly a pale white colour, sometimes with a hint of yellow, green, blue or mauve, and varies from nearly transparent to nearly totally opaque. Intense attractive colours are costly and the combination of four distinct colours in one carving is a desirable feature in the Far Eastern markets. A dark jadeite-diopside mixture is sometimes referred to by the name chloromelanite, from *chloro* meaning "green" and *melanite* meaning "black".

CRYSTAL SYSTEM: both nephrite and jadeite are monoclinic.

HABIT: both are fibrous aggregates, but nephrite is called actinolite or tremolite if it is in single crystals. Jadeite individual crystals are often visible in carvings. Both these minerals are normally found as stream-worn pebbles, their outer surfaces frequently discoloured by the effects of erosion.

HARDNESS: nephrite: 5.5–6.5 varying with heating, weathering and erosion; jadeite: normally 7, but can be softer at the boundary points between large single crystals.

CUT: mostly in cabochons or carved in a wide variety of ways.

History

Nephrite jade has been prized by the people of China since the dawn of recorded history, as is clear from those tombs of the neolithic periods and the earliest Chinese dynasties which continue to be discovered. It is quite common for a burial of a lesser nobleman to yield over fifty carved jade amulets and ritual objects.

This stone was worked and used by all the major Chinese dynasties until the end of imperial rule. Large quantities of jade carvings exist, and many day-to-day objects were fashioned in this gem for wealthy patrons. Ritual objects were frequently used and many have survived to the present day and are preserved in the world's principal museums.

A "chicken bone" nephrite jade libation cup. Chinese, approximately 1000 years old (Nephrite turns opaque greyish-white when burnt at high temperature in a fire). Photograph courtesy of E.A. Jobbins.

A delicately made white nephrite jade vase, in the form of a lotus plant. Chinese, 18th century. Photograph courtesy of E.A. Jobbins.

Astronomical instruments and even weapons were crafted in jade, and the extraordinary bronze vessels made during the Shang and Chou periods were frequently copied in this tough gemstone. Entire suits of jade panels connected by gold wires were made in an attempt to preserve the royal body encased within it.

Dating Chinese jade carvings is very difficult, as many styles and forms were copied over a period of several thousands of years. The only pieces of reliable known date are those that have been properly excavated from sites where other material and information are found to confirm the date of the burial.

The experienced collector learns that careful observation of the material, its colour, form and method of execution will give invaluable indications of the probable period to which the carving belongs. The history and use of jade in China is very complex and the reader is referred to specialist books on this subject.

A discoloured nephrite jade tiger. Chinese, approximately 1800 B.C. Photograph courtesy of E.A. Jobbins.

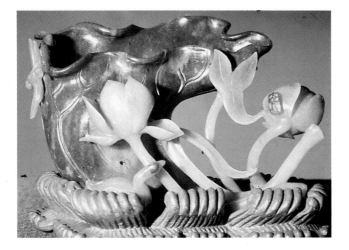

A bi-colour grey and white nephrite jade-lotus shaped water pot, used for washing brushes. Chinese, 18th century. Photograph courtesy of E.A. Jobbins.

In around 1750 the Chinese under the rule of the Emperor Chien en Lung (1735–95) began importing some beautifully coloured jade into China from Burma, and much to everyone's amazement this material turned out to be jadeite. It was of similar appearance, but generally of much superior quality and colour to most of the Pre-Columbian material. It has now been satisfactorily established that virtually all Burmese jadeite worked in China dates from 1750 and that all earlier Chinese jade carvings are made of nephrite. Jadeite has been and is still worked in China, and is regarded by the majority of modern Chinese as the most desirable variety of jade.

Jadeite and a number of green gemstones with a similar appearance were used extensively in the Pre-Columbian cultures. As these civilizations did not leave any written records it is difficult to know the precise role, place and function that jadeite objects played in their lives. The belief still persists today that a jadeite amulet will relieve discomfort and disease of the kidneys. There are a number of specialist books which examine the use of jadeite by this culture in more detail, and the interested reader is referred to these.

Jadeite was used extensively in Western jewellery in the 1920s, and carved pendant pieces were frequently set as the centrepiece of a complex design, usually made of platinum, and set with pearls and assorted gemstones. Boxes were often set with carved panels and small ruby studs were inserted through the piercing to provide a pleasing contrast.

The Maori people of New Zealand have used the green nephrite found in the southern island of that country for making war axes and ceremonial carvings. A few examples still exist today dating back to the seventeenth century. A number of these distinctive carvings can be seen in major museums.

Sources

Nephrite is a plentiful material, with many sources, and has been used recently for a large range of lower-priced jewellery. The bulk of this material is from the USSR, British Columbia, and New Zealand. It is worked in vast quantities in the Far East in Taiwan

Nephrite jade incense burner. 18th century. Photograph courtesy of C. Cavey.

and Hong Kong, and now workshops of mainland China are producing large numbers of carvings for export.

Jadeite is very scarce, and the main source is still the stone tracts of Upper Burma, which have yielded virtually all the material that is, and was, worked in China. There is little evidence of fine material being found today in the Central American region. The finest green stone from this locality seems to have been found during the Mixtec period (eighth to twelfth centuries). Jadeite is found today in small quantities in Japan, Mexico, and the state of California, USA. Jadeite is currently in commercial mining production in Guatemala and the USSR, but the bulk of this material is of low quality.

Treatment of Jade

Nephrite can be stained but this is rarely encountered (see coloration section above). Jadeite is stained in a variety of ways, normally to simulate the desirable green and lavender colours. The staining of green jadeite is much easier to detect than the staining of lavender jadeite.

Synthetic Jade

Synthetic nephrite is not currently produced. Synthetic jadeite has been manufactured as an experiment by the General Electric Company in the USA, but no material has ever been commercially available.

Left: A Mogul (Indian) style Chinese nephrite jade libation cup on its original carved wooden stand. The Chinese in the 17th–18th centuries carved many jades for the Mogul Emperors, and the style sometimes persisted and was adapted for Chinese domestic objects. Photograph courtesy of C. Cavey.

Above: Carved celadon-coloured nephrite jade mountain, Chinese, possibly 17th century. Photograph courtesy of E.A. Jobbins.

Right: A range of carved and polished examples of jadeite, showing some of the more popular natural colours. Photograph courtesy of C. Cavey.

Principal Gemstones that Can Simulate Jade

BOWENITE: widely sold under the misnomer "new jade". This is a hard form of the mineral serpentine and has been carved by the Chinese for a number of centuries. It can make a very convincing jade simulant and normally has an appearance similar to nephrite. This material can be as hard or harder than nephrite, so testing a suspect carving for hardness with a file or knife blade will not be conclusive.

WILLIAMSITE: a dark-green soft form of serpentine that can simulate jade.

SMARAGDITE, MAW-SIT-SIT, AND SAUSSURITE: can be confused with nephrite and jadeite.

EMERALD: can be mistaken for green jadeite, as can tourmaline in various colours.

HYDROGROSSULAR GARNET: makes a convincing jade simulant. The feldspar amazonite can have a similar outward appearance to jadeite.

CHALCEDONIES and a number of varieties of the mineral quartz: frequently misidentified as varieties of jade by unsuspecting dealers.

Various forms of common opal: can make convincing jade simulants.

Fluorite, turquoise and malachite can be mistaken for jade.

There are a number of very convincing glass imitations of jade, particularly of jadeite. Many were developed by the Chinese as a cheap jade substitute.

Altogether there are over forty different stones that can make very convincing jade simulants. Given the many methods of staining and enhancing the colour of the two jade minerals, comprehensive gemmological testing is absolutely essential before any assumptions can be made.

PERIDOT

Peridot is a gemstone which belongs to the mineral group olivine. These gems are part of a series of two distinct mineral varieties, fayalite and forsterite, and they may therefore have differing properties. The ancient topaz was almost certainly the stone that we now call peridot. The word peridot has been used to describe this gemstone since the medieval period when it was known as *peridota*. Yellowish peridots were called chrysolite, and some considerable confusion arose because this same name was also used to describe yellow chrysoberyl.

The general name peridot is usually applied to all gem varieties of the olivine group, although the term olivine is still acceptable to describe this gemstone. For a number of years "brown peridots" were mined in Sri Lanka. In the early 1950s these stones were found to be a completely different mineral, and they are now known as sinhalites.

CHEMICAL COMPOSITION: Magnesium or Iron Silicate.
COLOURS: almost yellow, pale green to deep green, brownish.

CRYSTAL SYSTEM: orthorhombic.
HABIT: mainly as grains, water-worn pebbles and fragments; rarely as distinct crystals.
HARDNESS: 6.5–7.0.
CUT: normally faceted, sometimes in cabochons, rarely engraved or carved.

History

The gemstone we know today as peridot was called topaz in the ancient world. It was used in the breastplate of the Jewish High Priest, and there are a number of Biblical references to it as well.

In the medieval period the names were reviewed and the word topaz was applied to a completely different gemstone. Peridot was also known as the chrysolite. In the seventeenth century a quantity of chrysoberyl came on to the market from Brazil, and was sold as chrysolite. This name is no longer used by gemmologists, and today peridots should not be referred to as chrysolites.

Apart from this gemstone's place as the birthstone

for the month of August, there is little evidence that it was employed in medicines, or specifically to cure any ailments. The confusion caused by the various names which were applied to this and other gems precludes attributing any specific properties to it.

Sources

The ancient locality of St John's Island (now known as Zebirget), which lies in the Red Sea off the coast of Egypt, was the chief locality for this gemstone in the ancient world. As olivine is a principal component of many volcanic rocks the impure form of peridot is found in a number of locations worldwide. Burma and Sri Lanka have produced many fine large stones. One of the largest peridot deposits exists in Chihuahua, Mexico. This gem is also mined in the USA in Arizona, California, New Mexico, Massachusetts and Hawaii. A large quantity of fine gem material has recently been mined in Norway, and many other minor localities exist in various parts of the world.

A peridot crystal, three faceted gemstones, one 18th-century intaglio ring, all standing on an olivine rock. Photograph courtesy of E.A. Jobbins.

Treatment of Peridots

Peridots are not subject to many forms of treatment. Rough peridot is frequently oiled to hide cracks and inclusions. Peridots have two planes of weakness and they scratch and chip easily.

Synthetic Peridots

Synthetic peridot is not produced commercially.

Principal Gemstones that Can Simulate Peridots

TOURMALINE, CHRYSOBERYL, BERYL, AND GREEN ZIRCON: can look like peridot.
GARNET-TOPPED DOUBLETS, PASTE, AND YELLOW-GREEN SYNTHETIC SPINELS: have been made to simulate this gemstone.

MALACHITE

The name malachite is derived from the Greek word *malakhe*, which is the name of the mallow plant. The green colour, appearance, and the bitterness to the taste of this mineral is probably why it is named after this herb. Malachite when ingested is quite poisonous, and the reader is advised not to attempt to verify these facts by practical demonstration.

CHEMICAL COMPOSITION: Copper Carbonate.
COLOURS: green in numerous shades to almost black.
CRYSTAL SYSTEM: monoclinic.
HABIT: normally layers and masses of stalagtitic material, sometimes as grains and microscopic crystals. Rarely as distinct crystals, but more commonly as pseudomorphs after crystals of the bright- to dark-blue copper mineral azurite. Sometimes malachite and azurite are intimately mixed, and this material is referred to as azurite/malachite.
HARDNESS: 3.5–4.5 (can be lower for non-gem material).
CUT: cabochon cut, carved and engraved. In grand palaces malachite is used in inlaid pillars, fireplaces, tables, and so on.

History

Malachite was cut and used as beads by the ancient Egyptians, and a few survive which date back to 1500 BC, although there is evidence that it was mined in Suez and Sinai as early as 4000 BC.

It appears possible that the term *smaragdus* (used to describe virtually all green gemstones in the ancient world) was used to describe objects made from malachite. Several classical authors refer to 50-foot columns covered in this gemstone, and it is unlikely that any other material would have been available to these civilizations in such quantity.

This gemstone was employed in Europe in talismans to protect children against evil influences, and a piece

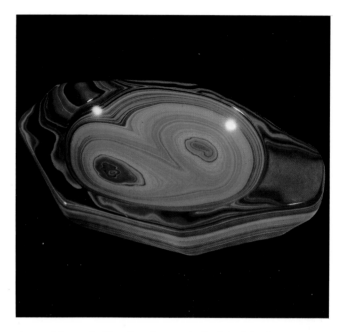

A superbly marked bowl cut from a single slab of the decorative gemstone malachite. This photograph illustrates the variation of colour and patterning of this gem which varies from layer to layer. Photograph courtesy of C. Cavey.

would be attached to the child's cradle to ensure that the occupant enjoyed a peaceful and uninterrupted night's sleep. The probable reasons for the birth of this belief are firstly that malachite is green in colour (a magical "elven" colour) and secondly that it is normally composed of layers of differing colours. When these stones are cut in cabochons, an eye effect can often be seen, hence their amuletic value for warding off the evil eye.

In Germany, the malachite was believed to protect the wearer from falling, and also to warn against approaching disaster by breaking into pieces (a property otherwise attributed only to turquoise). When engraved with the symbol of the sun, malachites were said to protect from enchantments and evil spirits, and to ward off attacks by venomous creatures.

This gem material is sometimes employed by artists for grinding into a green pigment, which makes a very stable green-coloured paint.

Russian mammelory malachite from the U.S.S.R. Photograph courtesy of B.S. Lloyd of Gregory, Bottley & Lloyd.

Sources

Malachite is found in many localities worldwide, but there are only a few major locations which are worthy of mention here. The current principal source of commercially mass-produced material is the mines of Zaïre in Africa.

The largest deposits of this mineral for many years were the mines in Mednorudyansk, in the USSR, which produced masses weighing in excess of 50 tons. Both Zambia and Namibia produce quantities of fine malachite, and some excellent crystallized specimens. Malachite is also mined in the states of Arizona, New Mexico, Tennessee, and Utah in the USA, and in Mexico, Australia, and Cornwall, England.

Treatment of Malachites

This gem material is sometimes hard-resin-coated to give it a hard, resilient outer layer. It is soft, porous, and can be very difficult to polish. Frequently cavities are opened when the material is being worked, and it is quite common practice in infill these with a mixture of malachite pieces, powder and hard resin. Entire objects are sometimes manufactured from similar resin-bonded small fragments. Many large antique *objets d'art* have malachite bases, pillars and components. In the majority of these the material is only a thin veneer made up of many small pieces all cemented together.

Synthetic Malachites

Synthetic malachite is not made commercially.

Principal Gemstones that Can Simulate Malachites

There are a number of copper minerals which can have a similar appearance to malachite. The copper mineral chrysocolla frequently contains a percentage of malachite, as does the eilat stone marketed in Israel. Chrysocolla quartz could on rare occasions be mistaken for this mineral. Convincing glass and plastic imitations of malachite are produced.

ZIRCON

The name zircon is probably derived from the Arabic *zerk*, or the Persian words meaning golden-coloured. This gemstone comes in a wide range of colours and is frequently mistaken for other gemstones. The name "jacinth" or "hyacinth" was also used to describe this gem.

Pale to colourless zircons were often called jargoons, and were used as a cheaply available diamond simulant. This ability to simulate diamond gained for the zircon an unhealthy reputation. The stigma increased early in this century with the extensive use of heat-treated colourless zircons in a wide range of low-quality gold jewellery.

Within the last twenty years, however, a new synthetically produced diamond simulant has come on the market. This is known to gemmologists as synthetic cubic zirconia. The trade and jewellers sometimes sell this product under various names, but a practice has developed of simply referring to it as zirconia. This has led once again to natural zircons beings relegated, by many people, into the class of a synthetic or imitation gemstone.

Natural zircons provide a wide range of beautiful natural gemstones and should never be regarded purely as a simulant.

CHEMICAL COMPOSITION: Zirconium Silicate plus other elements to colour.
COLOURS: virtually all colours. Green zircons normally contain a greater portion of rare earth elements and uranium. Some of these gems are mildly radioactive.
CRYSTAL SYSTEM: tetragonal.
HABIT: normally found as water-worn pebbles, but they occasionally occur in well-formed crystals.
HARDNESS: 6.5–7.5.
CUT: usually faceted, rarely as cabochons. Rarely carved or engraved.

History

The name Zircon has not always been applied to this gemstone and it was certainly known at some time at jacinth, hyacinth and jargoon. Hyacinth was the most commonly utilized name, and a number of properties were attributed to this gem.

In the Middle Ages hyacinths were supposed to help procure wisdom, honour and riches, and to assist the wearer in sleeping peacefully. The stone was also ground and used as an ingredient in various potions.

Crystals and cut stones demonstrating the colour range possible in zircons. Photograph courtesy of E.A. Jobbins.

Hyacinth was the recommended gem for inclusion in amulets for travellers, and was said to protect the wearer from plagues, wounds and injuries. In addition it was said to afford the travellers with a cordial reception wherever they went.

Like many gems it was said to grow dim and pale in the presence of danger, and was supposedly a powerful amulet against witchcraft spells, and against being struck by lightning. Indeed, it was regarded as so powerful that a mere wax impression taken from an engraved hyacinth was sufficient to do the same.

The name hyacinth was also used to describe hessonite garnets, and therefore not all these properties can be directly attributable to zircons.

Sources

There are many sources of zircons, and much of the material is extracted as a by-product from the mining of other gem materials, and occasionally from large-scale commercial mining for metals such as tin.

The principal area where gem-quality zircon is mined centres on the Far East, in Cambodia, Thailand, Burma, and Sri Lanka. Fine zircons are also mined in the African countries of Nigeria and Tanzania, and in Australia, a number of states in the USA, the USSR, Brazil, Korea, and Germany. Canada and Norway produce very fine crystals.

Treatment of Zircons

These gemstones are subject to a wide range of heat treatments, which have varying effects depending upon the original colour of the stones. The bulk of colourless zircons are produced by heating brown or golden material in air. Blue zircons are produced by heating brown zircons from Indo-China excluding contact with the air. Colours lighten and change in many of these stones when they are subject to heat treatment. Blue zircons will sometimes revert to brown after exposure to daylight over the course of a number of years. Reheating will occasionally restore the blue colour.

Synthetic Zircons

There has been no commercial production to date.

Principal Gemstones that Can Simulate Zircons

A number of gemstones can be mistaken for zircons, and the most common of these range from aqua-marines, topazes, tourmalines, sapphires, chrysoberyls, spinels, garnets, peridots, and sinhalites to a number of rarer gemstones.

Synthetic spinel, corundum and cubic zirconia can all be confused with colourless zircons. It is unlikely that anyone handling diamonds on a regular basis today would be deceived by a colourless zircon.

THE SERPENTINE GROUP

The general name serpentine is applied to a number of minerals within this group and is derived from a serpent-like patterning in some varieties of the stone. Most of these are decorative and ornamental materials that are not really suitable for gem use on a day-to-day basis.

There is a hard variety of serpentine called bowenite after the American G.T. Bowen (although he identified this material originally as nephrite jade). Bowenite is now available in large quantities as carved objects, and in various forms of jewellery.

Other varieties of serpentine include williamsite, chrysotile, lizardite, verd antique, antigorite, and clinochrysotile.

CHEMICAL COMPOSITION: Magnesium Silicate.
COLOURS: very variable, rarely in intense bright colours, usually pale shades, or opaque, green, orange, brown, grey, black, and white.
CRYSTAL SYSTEM: monoclinic.
HABIT: usually fibrous aggregates, in gem qualities.
HARDNESS: 2.5–6.5. Bowenites are usually between 4 and 6.5. It is worth mentioning here that some bowenites will easily resist being scratched by a knife blade. This is a test used by many art dealers for distinguishing jade (normally nephrite) carvings from those made from bowenite. In some cases true jades can be scratched with a knife blade, and in some bowenite will resist. The reader is warned that this test is not in the least conclusive.
CUT: usually cut as cabochons, carved and engraved. Faceted material is occasionally encountered.

History

There is little doubt that these materials have been used since the dawn of civilization. Some of the earliest surviving seals are made from varieties belonging to this group. The Egyptians, Babylonians, Assyrians, Chinese, Greeks, and Romans all used seal stones carved in these materials.

It is quite possible that engravers were working these stones in the belief that they were merely softer forms of other gems, such as quartz and jade. Many items made of these materials exist, and it is quite evident that each colour, pattern and variety was treated as a separate gem.

There is no lore relating specifically to serpentines, but there is little doubt that pieces made of this material have been worshipped and revered by many cultures.

Opposite: *A group of Chinese seals carved in a variety of serpentines. Many of these are incorrectly referred to as "soapstone" in the trade. The two seals on the left are 18th–19th century, the orange-coloured seal on the right is 10th century, the green seal in the foreground. 2nd century B.C. Photograph courtesy of C. Cavey.*

Sources

Serpentines are found in many areas throughout the globe. The gem varieties of bowenite are found in New Zealand, China, the USA, Afghanistan, and South Africa. A pale-green serpentine comes from Connemara, in Ireland, and is sometimes erroneously called "Connemara marble".

Treatment of Serpentines

Wax and plastic impregnation is common, and many carvings are stained in an attempt to simulate antiquity.

Synthetic Serpentines

There is no commercially produced material.

Principal Gemstones that Can Simulate Serpentines

More often than not serpentines are employed to simulate the rarer, harder, and more desirable gemstones. As these materials are relatively common they are less commercially desirable than the scarcer gems. Serpentines can easily be mistaken for jaspers, jades, and a number of other ornamental gem materials.

LAPIS-LAZULI

The name lapis-lazuli is an ancient one, the first part of the name, *lapis*, being a word for stone while the second part of the name, *lazuli* signifies the heavens. Its name is certainly derived from the intense blue colour which is characteristic of the best examples of this gem material.

Unlike many other gemstones, lapis-lazuli is composed of more than one mineral, and is therefore regarded as a rock. This material is, by virtue of its mixture, very varied in its structure, composition and general properties.

The principal mineral components of lapis-lazuli are the minerals lazurite, sodalite, hauyne, calcite and iron pyrites. There are other minerals present but these are usually in smaller proportions.

CHEMICAL COMPOSITION: variable, but the principal component is the mineral lazurite and this has a composition of Sodium Calcium Aluminium Silicate.
COLOURS: many shades of blue, sometimes grey and violet.
CRYSTAL SYSTEM: for lazurite, cubic.
HABIT: normally massive. Distinct crystals of lazurite are known but are very rare.
HARDNESS: 4–6.
CUT: cabochon cut, carved and engraved in a variety of ways.

History

This gemstone has been used in decorative jewellery and objects since the ancient Egyptian period. At that time it was very highly valued and there is good evidence that it was in relatively short supply. The famous burial mask of the boy king, Tutankamun, has lapis-lazuli inlaid around the eyes, but the rest of the blue inlay on the piece is composed of blue glass enamel, simulating this gem.

Lapis-lazuli is mentioned many times in the Bible and other religious texts, and it is most probable that this gemstone is the sapphire of the very ancient world (true sapphires are known to have been used in ancient Greece and Rome). This gem was one of those used in the breastplate of the Jewish High Priest, and we know it was used in many symbolical and talismanic objects in ancient Egypt.

The gem was utilized by many of the world's great civilizations, and examples still exist dating from the dawn of civilization.

The colour of this gem enabled it to be used in talismans and religious objects to symbolize the heavens. In drawing the wearer or perceiver of the stone closer to the gods or God, it helped protect them from the dark evil influences below.

Like the sapphire, the lapis-lazuli was looked on by some cultures as a stone symbolizing chastity. Indeed, many of the ancient properties of this gem are intimately mixed with those of sapphire.

Ground lapis-lazuli was used as an ingredient in various forms of eye wash, and as the principal ingredient in the artist's palette colour ultramarine.

A group of Chinese seals, carved in nephrite jade (white), amber (orange/brown), chrome-coloured jadeite (green), tourmaline (multi-coloured), lapis-lazuli (blue). 15th–20th centuries. Photograph courtesy of C. Cavey.

Opposite: *Carved lapis-lazuli head, representing "Night", mounted into a composite worked base. Executed in 1936 by Alfred L. Pocock. Photograph courtesy of Mrs W. Bottley.*

The value to the art world of such a blue pigment was incalculable, since the other blue pigments which were then available faded in bright light.

Sources

The principal locality for this gemstone is Badakshan, in Afghanistan, and it was the mines there that produced the material that is found in many objects from the ancient Egyptian civilizations. The same area still produces quantities of fine-quality material, although the colour of bulk-produced material is now

An engraved plate (dated 1657) representing a classical intaglio in lapis-lazuli, from the collection of L. Augustini. Photograph courtesy of C. Cavey.

A sample group of lapis-lazuli. In the foreground is a scarab which is over 4000 years old. The two intaglios are of classical Greco-Roman period, with 18th-century mounts. The Chinese seal is 18th century. All the material originated in Afghanistan. Photograph courtesy of C. Cavey.

dissimilar to that of ancient material. Lapis-lazuli is mined in commercial quantities in Chile and Argentina, in South America. The Argentinian material sometimes rivals the quality of the top Afghan grades. The USSR produces quantities of this gem, but it often has a much greater percentage of calcite present in its structure. The colour can be an intense bright blue, but is usually interspersed by brilliant white spots of calcite. Mongolia, Italy, the USA, Canada, Burma and Pakistan all produce small quantities of this gem material.

Treatment of Lapis-Lazuli

This material is quite porous and is therefore easily stained. Large masses frequently have a large percentage of their area formed of white calcite mixed with

A group of Ancient Egyptian scarabs. The top row are made of glazed soapstone, to imitate a variety of gems. The bottom row is made of (right to left) agate, fluorite, lapis lazuli, carnelian and amazonite. Photograph courtesy of C. Cavey.

the blue material. Staining these pieces results in the blue becoming more intense and the white calcite areas appearing to be pure lapis-lazuli. Staining is quite easily detected by experienced gemmologists. The heat treatment of some material to lighten its colour (when it was over-dark) has been reported.

Plastic impregnation is sometimes used to seal cracks and to facilitate polishing of very granular pieces.

Synthetic Lapis-Lazuli

This has been manufactured by Pierre Gilson. It is generally made to simulate the best jewellery-grade material. This is of a fine even rich blue colour with small particles of iron pyrites distributed evenly throughout the body of the gem.

A magnificent carving of a swimming sea lion in lapis-lazuli. The piece is executed from a single block and is over 14 inches long. Carving by G. Dreher. Photograph courtesy of P.V. Keane.

Principal Gemstones that Can Simulate Lapis-Lazuli

The mineral sodalite (one of the minerals that goes to form lapis-lazuli) is sometimes confused with this gemstone and a sintered synthetic spinel with gold inclusions was made by Pierre Gilson before he achieved true synthesis of this material. Stones of this kind are now scarce, but can be deceptive to the eye.

A BLUE-STAINED MARBLE: is the most commonly encountered simulant on the market today. It is made into boxes, beads and a wide variety of carvings.

A STAINED IMPURE FORM OF JASPER: most commonly used in the nineteenth century to simulate lapis lazuli, and is often referred to as "Swiss lapis".

BLUE GLASS IMITATIONS, SOMETIMES WITH GOLD LEAF FLECKS: have been made for many thousands of years.

A BLUE VARIETY OF CHALCEDONY, coloured by inclusions of the mineral dumortierite, and deep-blue sapphires: can be mistaken for this gemstone.

FLUORITE

The name of this material is derived from its ability to flow when melted, which occurs when commercial-grade fluorite is used as a flux during smelting metals.

This gem is very soft, fragile (it has four perfect cleavage planes) and is generally highly unsuitable as a true gem mineral. The truly remarkable colour range, size, and transparency of the gem-quality material, however, make it impossible to neglect as a material for cutting and carving.

The name fluorspar was originally used for this stone, but convention has now dictated that the accepted name is fluorite. The name "Blue John" is applied to a banded purple multi-crystalline fluorite from Derbyshire, England.

CHEMICAL COMPOSITION: Calcium Fluoride with various elements to colour.

COLOURS: this material comes in a very wide range of colours and is sometimes multi-coloured within the one piece. Bright distinct colours are not uncommon, with the exception of a distinct red. Colour-change material from blue to purple is quite common. Some varieties fluoresce in daylight imparting a blue-mauve overcolour to the base colour of the material.

CRYSTAL SYSTEM: Cubic.

HABIT: frequently in fine crystals, normally cubes with additional faces, sometimes octahedral, rarely dodecahedral. In veins and masses, often showing considerable colour variation.

HARDNESS: 4.

CUT: faceted, engraved, carved, and sometimes used as an inlay on large decorative items.

Fluorite. Green, fluorescing mauve in daylight, from the Heights mine Co. Durham, England. Photograph courtesy of B.S. Lloyd of Gregory, Bottley & Lloyd.

History

Fluorite has been carved, engraved and used for making a wide variety of objects, since the dawn of history. This gem, like so many others, was not known under its own name, but was regarded as a softer variety of the various other gemstones.

The ancient Egyptians carved statues and scarabs from this stone. The Romans prized cups made from banded purple fluorite above many of their other possessions. They believed that almost any quantity of alcoholic beverage could be consumed from these cups without the consumer suffering any intoxication.

The Chinese have, for over three hundred years, produced superb examples of carved fluorite statues, vases and urns. In Derbyshire in the eighteenth century Blue John was worked into fine vases and urns, and inlaid into tables, clocks, mirrors and a variety of furniture.

Powdered fluorite in water was administered to patients in the eighteenth century to help relieve diseases of the kidneys.

Sources

Fluorite is found in many localities across the globe, and only a few places can be mentioned here. A number of European countries produce fine examples, and some of the largest transparent single crystals come from the USA.

Mexico, South Africa, Thailand, China, Canada and Peru all produce fine material.

Treatment of Fluorite

Granular forms of banded fluorite such as Blue John are normally impregnated to hold them together before they are worked in any way. In the eighteenth century shellac was used for this purpose, but modern epoxy resins are now employed. Finished carvings can be resin-coated to improve their strength. Cabochons of Blue John are commonly quartz-capped to increase their resistance to wear.

Synthetic Fluorite

Large quantities of low-quality fluorite are manufactured for use by the steel-making industry. Transparent gem-quality fluorite is made by research laboratories and occasionally finds its way on to the market.

Principal Gemstones that Can Simulate Fluorite

The colour range of this material is such that many other gemstones can easily be mistaken for it. Its low hardness and lack of brilliance as a cut gemstone normally make it distinctive from most other gem materials. Some glasses can have a close appearance to fluorite, and feldspars, quartz and beryls may be mistaken for these gems. Chrome-green transparent fluorite makes a deceptive and convincing emerald simulant. Banded amethyst is commonly mistaken for Blue John.

PEARL

The name pearl originates from the Latin word *perula*. These gems are formed in a number of shell-bearing aquatic creatures. The formation of a pearl is begun as a defensive measure by the animal in an attempt to neutralize an irritation. In the case of natural pearls this is caused by small particles or creatures entering the shell and coming into contact with the body of the animal. The creature responds by secreting a liquid which envelops the irritant and hardens into layers of shell around it.

This process continues throughout the life of the creature, for as long as the pearl is embedded in the shell or body of the animal. As the animal and shell grow, so does the pearl enclosing the original irritant. In general, the more layers that make up the pearl, the better its quality and more desirable it becomes.

Pearls are found in a number of shell fish in salt and fresh waters. In addition to the many varieties of oyster, mussels, conches and clams can all produce material that is accepted as pearl.

CHEMICAL COMPOSITION: Calcium Carbonate (in

A view of a cultured-pearl farm in the Far East. Photograph courtesy of E.A. Jobbins.

93

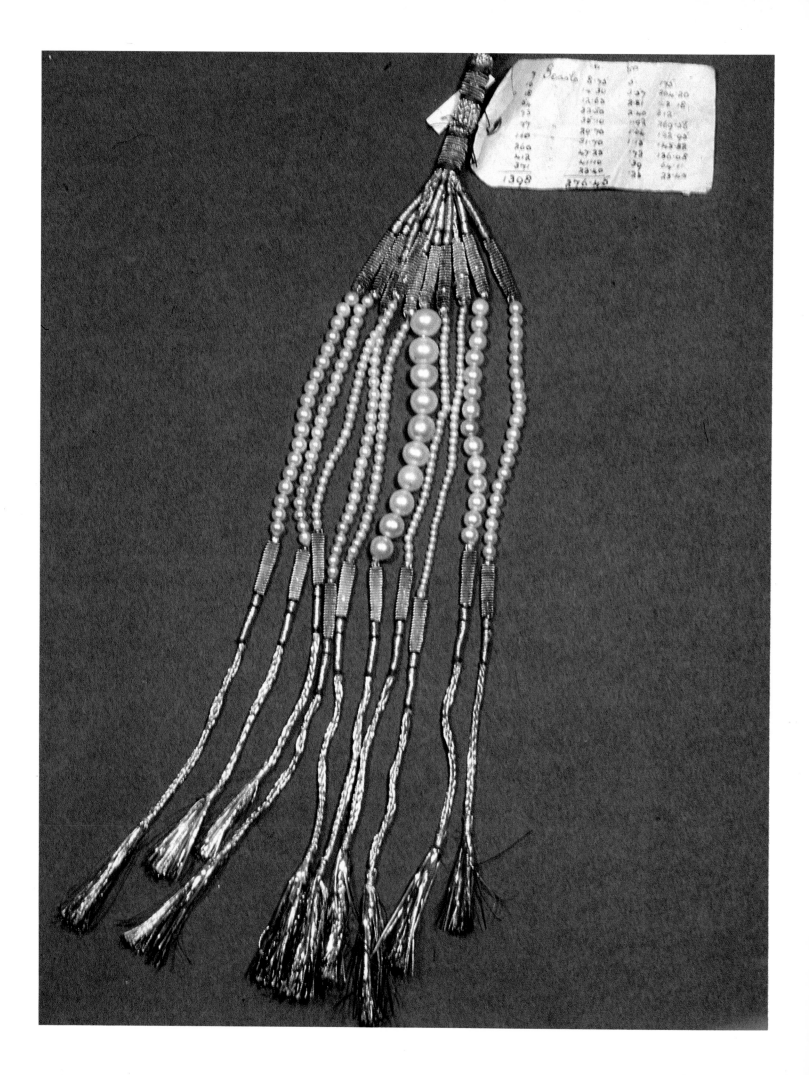

An engraved portrait of the Austro-Hungarian Empress Maria Theresa, in 1717. Note the bodice of her dress, which is totally smothered in jewels and pearls. Photograph courtesy of C. Cavey.

A portrait of Maria Luigia de Tassis, by Van Dyck. If compared with the styles of a few years earlier, the jewellery worn is relatively modest, and only consists of a single row of pearls and two pendant crosses, Circa 1630. Photograph courtesy of C. Cavey.

the form of aragonite) with various additives depending on the creature involved.

COLOURS: the majority of pearls are white with a slight tint of another colour, although almost all colours are possible. In the case of untreated natural pearls, the colour will relate to the colour of the animal's shell which produces the pearl. If the layers of pearl are thin (thin layers are quite translucent), the colour can then be determined by the colour of the nucleus.

TYPES OF PEARLS: pearls are normally regarded as round, but can come in an extraordinary range of shapes. Round pearls are formed when the irritant is trapped in the body of the animal away from the shell wall. These are sometimes cut in half (half pearls) and in other ways to facilitate mounting. A range of

Opposite: *A string of natural salt-water natural pearls known as a "Bombay bunch". Photograph courtesy of E.A. Jobbins.*

regular shaped pearls are known, and these are normally referred to by their shape.

Seed pearls are small pearls less than 0.05 carats in weight. If the nucleus is large and irregular, then the resultant pearl will take its shape, only becoming rounded off as many additional layers of pearl are deposited. These are known as baroque pearls.

When the irritant is sandwiched between the animal and its shell, the pearl produced will normally attach itself to the shell. These are called blister pearls, and have to be cut from the surface of the shell. A backing piece of "mother-of-pearl" (pearl shell), is usually cemented on to them to hide the cut surface.

Not all pearls have a pearly lustre, and the pink or orange or brown pearls produced by the conch have the appearance of polished coral, except for a "flame"-like structure which is usually present on their surface. The largest pearls in the world are produced by the giant clam, and can be several pounds in weight. These

A 19th-century engraved portrait of Queen Margaret, wife of James III of Scotland. Note the extensive use of gem-set jewels and pearls in her head-dress and garments. Medieval period. Photograph courtesy of C. Cavey.

have a similar appearance to the conch pearls but are normally white in colour.
HARDNESS: 2.5–3.0.

History

Archaeological evidence suggests that pearls have been used by man since the dawn of history. This gem was worn by the Jewish High Priest in his robe (*ephod*) and is mentioned on a number of occasions in the Bible. One of the most famous of quotations taken from the New Testament is of Jesus Christ telling his followers "cast not your pearls before swine". This is probably where "the pearls of wisdom" were born.

Few pearls exist today that predate the classical Roman period. This is mainly due to their inability to resist even the mildest of acids which are ever-present

A fine string of natural Scottish river pearls, with one large pearl sitting on the mussel shell at the rear. Photograph courtesy of E.A. Jobbins.

in the ground where most surviving examples have been excavated. Pearls can suffer from corrosion when worn on the skin, particularly in conjunction with certain cosmetics which are mildly acidic.

One of the famous stories in the lengthy and complex history of pearls is of Cleopatra removing a priceless large drop-shaped pearl earring, and dissolving it in her wine, in order to participate in the costliest feast of the day. It is unlikely that this pearl did readily dissolve unless it was first powdered. It is interesting to note how difficult it is to match a pair of fine pearl drops, and what an incredible difference in price there is still today between a single fine large pearl and a matched pair (the price for both almost doubles).

Pearls have been alluded to in literature since the earliest times, and have been employed for a number of purposes. They were used by some to procure oracular vision to enable them to interpret dreams. A dream involving pearls was, however, viewed with fear, as it was interpreted as a forewarning of the tears of grief. This interpretation probably owes its origin to the belief that pearls were formed by the tears of the gods falling from the heavens into the sea and then being preserved by the oysters.

Pearls have been used in medicines for a long period, and it was believed that when they were powdered and dissolved they would cure all manner of ailments. They were used for the cure of stomach complaints, for healing ulcers, and for the relief of pestilential fevers. They were even employed in the treatment of haemorrhage, and in some cases as an antidote to poison. In the Indian state of Bengal, it was believed that if they were worn by a virgin they would preserve her virtue.

Queen Elizabeth I of England possessed a number of dresses ornamented with many thousands of fine pearls, a few of which are rumoured to survive today, 400 years later, in the jewels of her present-day successor Elizabeth II.

There is a considerable mythology surrounding pearls and the interested reader is referred to specialist texts purely on this subject. One belief that still persists today is that pearls will lose their brilliance and lustre if they are not worn. This is not so, unless they are stored in contact with anything acidic. It is important to note here that much cotton wool, cardboard (from which boxes are made), and cloth, can all be slightly acidic. Owners of pearls are well advised to examine the wrapping, padding and boxes used for storing their jewels.

Sources

Natural sea-water pearls are the most commercially desirable and they are still found in the following areas.

Throughout the Persian Gulf area pearls have been harvested for thousands of years. These are dived for between the months of May and September, and are still collected by traditional methods. The pearls are usually sold on the local markets, and quantities are exported to Bombay, in India, for grading and drilling. The Red Sea used to be a source of fine pearls, but the pollution currently in this area has considerably reduced its oyster beds.

The Gulf of Manaar (between India and Sri Lanka) has been a source of fine pearls for over 2000 years. These beds still produce small quantities of fine-quality natural pearls.

The South Sea pearl fisheries situated in the area around Polynesia are currently producing a few large natural pearls. However, the bulk of these fisheries are now used to grow substantial numbers of large cultured pearls.

Australia has a number of pearl fisheries and produces some of the largest of all the natural pearls. The beds are now mainly used for mass production of large beaded cultured pearls.

The Japanese produce both salt-water and fresh-water pearls, and nucleated and non-nucleated cultured pearls in large quantities. Pollution is now

A pendant made from five high-quality pink pearls. These are not found in oysters, but come from the marine conch. Photograph courtesy of E.A. Jobbins.

limiting the further expansion of this productive area.

China is now producing quantities of nucleated and non-nucleated cultured pearls from salt-water and fresh-water fisheries.

Venezuela produces a range of natural and nucleated cultured pearls. These come in an assortment of colours varying from white to grey, bronze and black.

The Gulf of Mexico produces a number of fine natural pink pearls from the marine conch.

Fresh-water natural pearls are fished on a commercial basis in America in the Mississippi River and its tributaries, in Scotland, Ireland, France, Germany and Austria.

Treatment of Pearls

Pearls are often boiled in a range of bleaches to improve their colour and lustre. The dyeing of pearls to various colours is quite common. The immersion of a pearl overnight in silver nitrate will normally turn it brown, and with exposure to bright sunlight it becomes a blackish colour.

Natural pearls which are damaged by acidic skin or chipped and broken in everyday wear are sometimes "skinned". As the pearl is made up of many thin layers it is sometimes possible to remove a skin layer that has become broken, and restore the pearl to its full beauty, thereby reducing its size. Pearls (especially fresh-water varieties) can discolour when exposed to X-rays. X-ray photography is used to distinguish natural from cultured pearls.

Cultured Pearls

These are formed when an irritant is artificially introduced into the animal, which then forms a pearl around it. This process has been used for over 200 years to produce blister pearls in various shapes. These were normally grown over small metal models of Buddha, and were then cut out from the shell to be used as charms and amulets.

It was not until the early twentieth century that full round cultured pearls were made on a commercial basis. The pioneering work was carried out in Japan, and this country is still one of the world's leading producers. The problem of producing round cultured pearls was solved by the careful insertion of a round bead wholly into the flesh of the oyster. This was a delicate process, since it was all too easy to kill the creature during the operation.

The mass production of cultured pearls was perfected in the 1920s and resulted in a massive drop in the price of real pearls. It was this problem that facilitated the formation of the world's first gem-testing laboratories.

Today, cultured pearls are grown in two basic ways.

The traditional method of inserting a bead upon which the oyster grows its pearl layers is still employed and successfully produces round and shaped cultured pearls up to 40 millimetres in diameter. The longer the pearl is in the oyster, the thicker the skin and the better the quality and lustre.

The other principal method of cultured pearl production involves inserting a piece of flesh from another oyster into the recipient, and a pearl will grow around this nucleus. These are known as "non-nucleated cultured pearls", and are now produced in vast quantities. The bulk of these are baroque (irregular in shape) and very occasionally a few are produced that are of a regular shape. Blister cultured pearls are referred to in the trade as mabé pearls.

Principal Gemstones that Can Simulate Pearls

There are no natural gemstones that could in normal circumstances be mistaken for varieties of pearl, although strange concretions that have a remarkably similar structure to pearls do exist. Round ivory concretions sometimes found in elephant tusks have been referred to as "elephant pearls". Strange round concretions found in caves have a similar structure to pearls and are called "cave pearls". However, none of these have the beautiful pearl lustre seen in the range of true pearls.

Glass imitation pearls have been made for a number of years and can be quite convincing to the inexperienced eye. These were originally made from a hollow bead of glass coated on the inside with a lacquer (*essence d'orient,*) mainly composed of fish scales, and then wax-infilled. Modern imitations are made of a glass bead nucleus coated with layers of *essence d'orient*.

AMBER

The name amber is derived from the Arabic word *anbar* which was then adapted to its present English form in the Middle Ages. Amber is not a mineral, but is a hardened fossil tree resin. It varies considerably in composition, depending on which type of tree the resin was exuded from and the circumstances in which it has survived over the past 30 to 60 million years.

There are a number of names applied to amber, most of which relate to the physical appearance of the material. Some are derived from localities, and others from constituent acids that are physically present in its make-up.

In common with most of the other organically produced gem materials amber can be very difficult to test satisfactorily. Myths persist even today that only real amber will attract dust and small pieces of tissue paper. In fact virtually all hard resins and plastics will do the same thing, together with non-amber natural resins, and more recent fossil resins like the kauri gum from New Zealand.

CHEMICAL COMPOSITION: a mixture of Hydrocarbons, plus succinic acid, and various oils and resins.
COLOURS: most commonly amber yellow, and variations of yellow, brown, reddish and rarely distinctly red. Green, blue, and violet material is known, but most of these have a yellow amber base colour and owe their overall coloration to a daylight fluorescent effect. White, grey and black amber has been found. Extreme care should be exercised when buying any amber, and the reader is advised to be especially careful when buying unusually coloured amber articles.
CRYSTAL SYSTEM: none.
HABIT: normally as nodules and pieces of a relatively small size, but occasionally in fist size or larger pieces. Sometimes pieces of amber contain the fossilized remains of insects trapped in the resin. Flies, spiders and a variety of rather small creatures are quite commonly preserved inside pieces of this gem. Larger insects and, very rarely, tree frogs, toads, lizards, and so on, have also been found encased in amber, but they usually have enough strength to escape from this sticky grave. It is wise to note here that for several years collectors have been avidly purchasing amber for its inclusions, and a number of convincing fakes, containing a wide variety of insects and other creatures, have been manufactured and marketed.
HARDNESS: 2.0–2.5.
CUT: faceted, cabochoned, carved, engraved, and used as an inlay on furniture.

History

Amber has a very diverse history, and is known to have been worn and valued by people in the Stone Age. It is found in jewellery of many cultures and was in common use in the major civilizations throughout Europe, the Middle East, Asia, and the Far East. Amber was not only employed in jewellery but used in talismans and in a wide range of medicines.

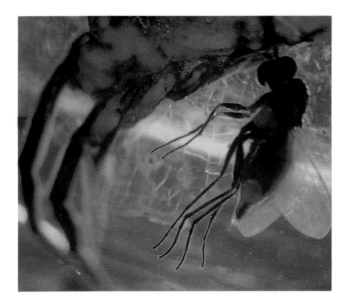

Baltic amber with an entrapped fly. This insect lived over 30 million years ago. Photograph courtesy of E.A. Jobbins.

99

Amber and ivory inlaid monstrance. North German, 17th century. Photograph courtesy of E.A. Jobbins.

number of important historical paintings.

Many beliefs and superstitions surround the history of this material. It is inappropriate to catalogue any but a few examples here. However, I hope these are sufficient to whet the reader's appetite, and anyone who is interested is referred to specialist books on this subject.

Sources

The Baltic States of the USSR, Poland, Sweden, Denmark and Germany all produce what is generally known as Baltic amber. England has a catchment area of Baltic amber on its East Coast. There are undersea Baltic deposits in which amber weathers out and floats across the North Sea, to be deposited on the beaches.

Old deposits exist in Mexico and the Lebanon, and amber is occasionally found in Canada and Alaska.

Burma produces a range of material, but is chiefly famous for rare red amber, which is sometimes found in pieces of immense size (several feet across).

The relatively new deposits of the Dominican Republic are producing an enormous range of material, sometimes with extraordinary insect and animal inclusions. Some of the finest blue, green and violet fluorescent amber comes from this locality.

The ancient Greeks believed that amber was formed annually by the mourning of the Heliades who shed tears for their deceased brother Phaëthon. The tears supposedly metamorphosed into poplars, which oozed amber which solidified under the rays of the sun.

Pieces of amber that exhibited natural markings which were similar to the initials of prominent persons, or that could be related to religious symbols, portents or signs, were very highly valued. Many amulets were made for the protection of the dead in the afterlife, and ancient amber cups, bowls, jewellery, and sword pommels have all survived intact after being buried with their owners.

Amber was distilled and its oils used in medicines. It was also burnt to release aromatic odours to relieve congestion and diseases of the lungs. Many references can be found to this material in old books on distillation, and amber oil is still used today in some medicines. Amber was also distilled to produce some of the finest picture varnishes, and these were used on a

Treatment of Amber

This material is subject to a wide range of treatments. Amber is in a permanent state of oxidation. This normally results in a change of colour on the exposed surfaces of the material. Amber which has been exposed to the rigours of oxidation for several thousands of years will normally darken throughout the whole body of the material. Not all amber that is sealed in tombs oxidizes, and examples of Ancient Egyptian and Minoan amber exist which have not changed to any great extent.

A number of heat-treatment processes will darken amber after it has been worked. Some of these will induce attractive large water-lily-shaped cracks to

Opposite: *A naturistic carved fruit in amber, which has been engraved from the rear through a tiny opening in the reverse. This group is entitled "The Birth of the Fairies", carved in 1926 by Alfred L. Pocock. Photograph courtesy of Mrs W. Bottley.*

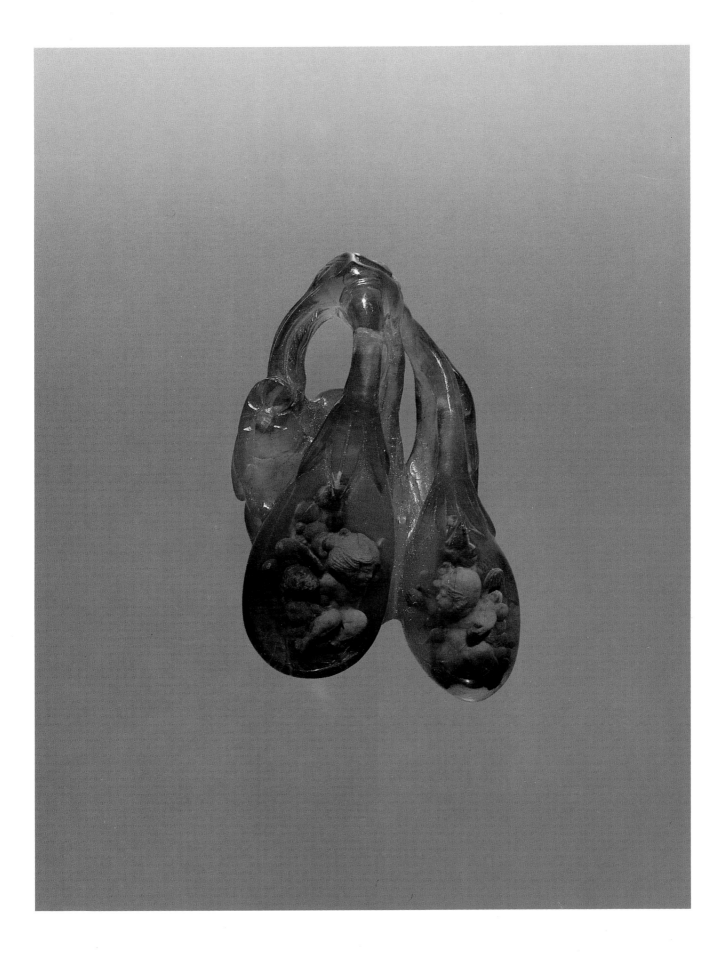

appear. Amber is stained, coated, melted, pressed, resin-bonded with modern epoxy resins, and sometimes it is sold as small natural pieces suspended in transparent plastic.

Testing amber requires many years of experience, technical knowledge and a familiarity with the many known types and forms of natural and treated ambers and similar resins.

Synthetic Amber

True synthetic amber is not produced commercially.

Principal Gemstones that Can Simulate Amber

Amber is very light in weight in relation to its size, and it is therefore quite easy to exclude a number of amber-coloured gemstones, which are proportionately too heavy to effectively simulate this gem. Amber is also warm to the touch and natural crystalline gem materials are usually relatively cold.

NATURAL COPALS: and in some instances modern tree resins, can be mistaken for true amber. Kauri gum, a fossil pine resin (about 300,000 years old) from New Zealand makes a convincing amber imitation.

PLASTICS, EPOXY RESINS: and similar materials are made to simulate amber. A phenol-formaldehyde

An assortment of Baltic amber found on the Norfolk coast of England, and jewellery made from similar material. Photograph courtesy of E.A. Jobbins.

resin, commonly called Bakelite, was produced in large quantities in the early years of this century. A number of types of this resin were made to simulate amber. By far the bulk of "amber" necklaces that filter back on to the market through the antiques trade are composed of this material. It was exported throughout the world and African tribal necklaces and Tibetan ancestral beads are commonly made of this simulant.

BLOND TORTOISESHELL: is a substance made from bonded plates taken from the underbelly of the marine hawksbill turtle. This can make a convincing amber simulant. Stained bull's horn beads are manufactured in Africa to simulate Burmese red amber.

GLASS IMITATIONS: are made, but are poor compared with resins and plastics.

IVORY

The name ivory is derived from the latin word *eboris*. In common with the other organic gem materials, ivory varies considerably in compositon, form and structure.

Ivory comes from a range of animals, although it is primarily associated with elephants. This is probably due to the fact that elephant tusks provide by far the largest and heaviest single pieces of this material (with the exclusion of mammoth tusks).

Quantities of fossil ivory are found with the remains of the woolly mammoth. These tusks, if complete, far exceed those of the elephant's in size and weight. However, they are normally found in a fragmented state due to weathering and the corrosive effects of time. In the inner areas of these tusks, the basic ivory can be almost indistinguishable from everyday elephant ivory. A naturally blue-stained variety of this fossil ivory is called odontolite and makes a passable simulant for the gem turquoise.

The next most common source of ivory is the large teeth of the hippopotamus, which provide a very white fine-grained high-quality ivory. There are two basic sets of large teeth, one curved and the other straight. The tusks of the wild boar are quite similar in outward appearance, but are of a smaller size. These are composed of a lower-grade, coarse-grained ivory.

There are three basic types of ivory from marine mammals, and the most common of these are the tusks of the walrus. Tusks from these animals can be as long as three feet and have a peculiar central core. The largest predator in the sea is the sperm whale, which has a set of over fifty large teeth. The largest of these teeth can be over 7 inches in length.

One of the most curious forms of ivory must surely be that from the narwhal. The male animal usually has one elongated tusk which is twisted throughout its length and protrudes some distance (like a spear) from

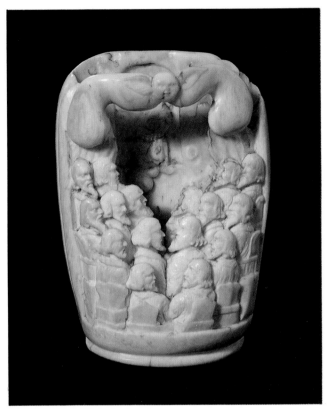

A carved religious scene executed on a marine ivory sperm whale tooth. Dutch, circa 1550. Photograph courtesy of C. Cavey.

A Madonna and Child carved in elephant ivory, showing dehydration, discoloration and the effects of age. European, 12th century. Photograph courtesy of C. Cavey.

the side of its head. These tusks are sometimes up to 14 feet in length. The discovery of narwhal tusks washed up on beaches in the ancient world almost certainly gave birth to the myths of the legendary unicorn.

There are several forms of hard nut which have been referred to as vegetable ivory. They are not of a similar chemical composition to any of the animal ivories, so the use of this name is misleading and these materials cannot be classed as true ivories.

Most forms of ivory are often referred to simply by that name. It is more helpful to the collector and researcher if a prefix of the source animal's name is included.

CHEMICAL COMPOSITION: Calcium Phosphate with variations.

COLOURS: usually white to cream yellow and brown, but it can be stained any colour.

CRYSTAL SYSTEM: none.

HABIT: all ivory is produced from the large or enlarged teeth (tusks) of animals. Human teeth are made of ivory but are too small to be used in a similar fashion to the large tusks and teeth of the ivory-bearing mammals. They have, however, been used for many years in jewellery by primitive tribesmen (the practice of wearing the teeth of a vanquished enemy was quite common). Human milk teeth are sometimes encountered set in Western jewellery as mementos.

HARDNESS: 2–3.

CUT: cabochon cut, carved, engraved, turned, and inlaid in a wide variety of ways.

103

Superbly executed cameo portraits in elephant ivory of Henry IV of France and his wife Marie de'Medici. Dieppe, France, circa 1880. Photograph courtesy of C. Cavey.

History

Since men began hunting in the Stone Age, they have worn the teeth of the animals they slaughtered for food. As they became more adept at catching game and trapping larger creatures they were able to acquire the tusks of the wild boar, and eventually those of the elephant.

Superb examples of carved ivory are known from the ancient Egyptian, Chinese, Babylonian, Minoan, Greek and Roman civilizations. Ivory is a very versatile material, and works of very good quality and great delicacy are not uncommon. There were many carving centres for ivory within Europe and several countries developed their own styles and distinct form of work. Major carving centres were also developed in China and Japan, and vast quantities of material are still worked in these centres today.

There are many beliefs surrounding ivory tusks, and the teeth of various large, sometimes dangerous animals. In the nineteenth and twentieth centuries the possession of a pair of bull elephant tusks was certainly regarded as a major prize among rich Europeans. These were usually obtained by people who went on safaris to various parts of Africa to shoot these animals for sport.

A considerable number of elephants have been destroyed over the past few years and there is now an official ban in many parts of the world on the sale of elephant ivory products. This has resulted in pressure on the other ivory-bearing animals, as the carving industries look for new

An extraordinary agate showing a patterning resembling the Madonna holding the infant Christ at the top of a staircase. The frame is made of hippopotamus ivory. It is set with silver-mounted rose-cut diamonds, and natural crystals of aquamarine. Green prophyry base. Photograph courtesy of C. Cavey.

An ivory portrait of the gem collector and Empress of Russia, Catherine The Great. Late 18th century. Photograph courtesy of C. Cavey.

legitimate sources of raw material, so that they too are becoming a cause for concern.

There is an immense quantity of superb work in this material, dating from the dawn of history to the present day, and it is impossible to ignore the important place that ivory has played throughout history.

The reader is referred to specialist works on specific areas of the history and use of ivory.

Sources

Elephant ivory is produced from both the African and the Indian elephant. African elephants are normally larger and consequently have bigger tusks. Hippopotamus is an indigenous species in Africa, and wild boar are found throughout Europe, Asia, and the Far East.

Marine ivory is found throughout the world's oceans, but the principal sources are the Arctic areas.

Treatment of Ivory

Ivory can be softened in acid so that it will peel as a veneer. These pieces are usually pressed to produce thin ivory sheets which are used as inlays and as a background material in miniature painting. Ivory is quite porous and is stained in many colours. Carvings which are designed to have an "antique look" are often stained in strong tea.

Powdered ivory is burnt to produce a very fine pigment known as "ivory black". This has an intense black hue and is regarded as one of the best black pigments.

Synthetic Ivory

True synthetic ivory is not manufactured.

Principal Gemstones that Can Simulate Ivory

Only a few natural gemstones simulate ivory. Varieties of jasper and coral can sometimes appear to be similar to ivory. There is a material known as "hornbill ivory", which is obtained from a large horny growth above the beak of this bird. Although it is of a pale-yellow ivory colour, it is mainly composed of a compact mass of fibres, and these are made of feather-making material (which is similar to hair). It is therefore not a true ivory, but is a much scarcer and rarer material than any of the animal ivories.

BONE: from various animals, stag horn and the corozo and doum-palm nuts, all make convincing ivory simulants.

A number of resins, plastics and other man-made products are created to simulate ivory. Many of these can be very convincing, and the reader is warned here of the number of very good-quality fake carvings that are currently available on the world market.

PRECIOUS CORAL

The general name coral covers a whole range of material, the bulk of which is soft, brittle, fragile and totally unsuitable as a gem material. The precious corals are harder and compact, and will to some extent resist the rigours of daily use. Coral is formed from the build-up of many small skeletons of microscopic animals called coral polyps.

The word coral is derived from the Greek *korallion* and the Latin *corallum*. Precious corals are quite rare and the bulk of these are found at considerable depth. The darkest red corals are called "oxblood" and the pale pinkish-white are called "angel skin".

CHEMICAL COMPOSITION: Calcium Carbonate (corals are composed of the mineral calcite, pearls are made of the mineral aragonite). Black and golden varieties are of a different structure from the other precious corals, and are made mainly of conchiolin.
COLOURS: white, pink, red, dark red, brown and black and in many shades and tones of these colours. Blue and an iridescent golden coral are known.
CRYSTAL SYSTEM: multi-crystalline but the underlying structure is trigonal.
HABIT: as branches, usually thin and spiky, but more rarely as thick branches sometimes several inches in diameter.
HARDNESS: 3–4.
CUT: cut in cabochons, carved and engraved in a variety of forms, rarely faceted, but then usually as beads and drops.

History

Red precious coral has been used in talismans and amulets from the dawn of history. Large numbers of coral beads and amulets have survived in ancient Egyptian burials.

Red corals have been held in high esteem, most probably because of their near blood-red colour. Beads and branches of this material were always given to the young children of the wealthy for their protection. It was used as a decoration on armour by Gaulish chiefs, in the belief that it would stem the flow of blood from their wounds. In India and Tibet corals have been used for several millennia as potent amulets to ward off the evil eye.

If the gem was worn next to the skin, it would supposedly become pale and lose its colour at the threat of serious illness or when the owner actually became ill. In Japan coral was dissolved in various acids and then imbibed, as this treatment was reckoned to clarify, purify and cleanse the blood.

A range of carved items in ivory (white), coral (red), jet (black). Photograph courtesy of E.A. Jobbins.

Coral was also taken to ease pain in the stomach and liver, and was said to stop all the fluxes of the belly and womb. It was administered in a quantity of ten grains as a cure for epileptic attacks in young children. It was also used to counteract poisons, to dispel witchcraft, and to protect from tempests and robbers.

A curious use was made of powdered coral, which was mixed with seed corn, and then sown. This supposedly protected the crops from blight, caterpillars, locusts, and even thunderstorms!

Red coral in particular was used in many items made for children, even up to the early twentieth century. Coral-mounted silver rattles are still in great demand, and the belief in the magical, talismanic and beneficial effects of this gem still strongly persists in the modern world.

There are many other supposed virtues attributed to coral, and they are too plentiful to list here, but the reader is referred to other works for additional information on this subject.

Sources

Precious corals are found in the deep waters of the Mediterranean Sea, and in the waters of the Persian Gulf, and Far East. Black coral is mined on the island of Hawaii, off the coast of Cameroon, and in parts of Indonesia. Golden coral is also mined in Hawaii.

Treatment of Coral

The staining of this material to improve its colour has been a recognized practice for many years. It is difficult to stain the deeply-coloured gem varieties, but pale shades will take on an overall colour, although this will be a deeper hue in cracked areas where the pigment can penetrate more readily.

In addition to staining, plastic impregnation of cavities and broken areas is quite a common practice, and occasionally entire items are made of powdered coral suspended in a resin base material.

Corals are easily attacked and dissolve in nearly all acids. Acidic skin and combinations of sweat and perfumes can remove the polish on coral beads. In acidic atmospheres all untreated corals will lose their lustre. Resin-coating and impregnation will assist corals to resist attack by acids.

Synthetic Coral

Although there is a substance manufactured and marketed under the name of "synthetic coral", the material currently produced is aragonite-based, and therefore it is not strictly classified as a true synthetic. This product is similar in colour to and has the general overall outward appearance of natural coral, but it has a totally different internal structure.

Principal Gemstones that Can Simulate Coral

The so-called "synthetic coral" is the closest simulant to the natural product. Porous common corals are sometimes stained and resin-bonded to simulate this material.

BONE, IVORY, MARBLE, AND CALCITE: are all products that are occasionally stained to imitate precious coral.

CARNELIAN AND JAPSER: can have a coral-like apperance, and sometimes jasper will replace fossil corals, taking on the internal patterning and structure.

Convincing glass, plastic, and resin imitations of corals are made in quantity.

JET

The name jet is derived from Gagates, the Greek name for an area of Lycia in Asia Minor, which was called after the River Gagas.

Jet is a compact, black form of brown coal or lignite, and it is this extra hardness which has made it suitable as an ornamental material. It is an organic product, being formed from the pressed remains of certain plants and trees that lived many millions of years ago. Like coal, jet is combustible, and it is usually necessary in the case of this gem to employ destructive methods of gem-testing to prove the nature of the stone.

In Prussia, jet was known as "black amber", and was

An engraved plate from 1741 of the Kaaba at the Grand Mosque in Mecca. The letter A signifies the point at which "the Black Stone" (a meteorite) is set in the wall of this holy shrine. Photograph courtesy of C. Cavey.

A group of bezoars, owned by the Austro-Hungarian Emperor Rudolph II. These were used to neutralize poisons placed in liquids. Photograph courtesy of C. Cavey.

A group of natural gem materials, all of which show a cross-shaped form. In the top centre are two examples of the gemstone chiastolite (a variety of andalusite). The other cross-shaped crystals are of a mineral known as staurolite. Photograph courtesy of C. Cavey.

sold as such to unwary customers but this name is no longer in use today.

CHEMICAL COMPOSITION: Organic Carbon (not a mineral).
COLOURS: usually black, sometimes brownish.
CRYSTAL SYSTEM: none.
HABIT: usually as seams, fragments and water-worn pebbles.
HARDNESS: 2.5–4.0.
CUT: can be faceted, engraved, carved, and cut in cabochons.

History

Objects made from this ornamental material were created in the pre-Roman period in northern Europe. Later on jet was certainly used in talismans and amulets, but it was not until the second half of the nineteenth century that it became very popular, when it was mass-produced for use in mourning jewellery.

This material was used in a variety of medicines. Powdered and mixed with beeswax it had a reputation as a sovereign remedy for reducing swelling in tumours. Powdered and mixed in wine it was given to relieve toothache. Jet was sometimes burnt to alleviate the congestion of the lungs.

Jet was worn as bracelets and was made into rosaries by monks, since it was seen as suitably modest in keeping with their vows of poverty.

Jet jewellery is still manufactured in various parts of the world, although the colour of the material limits its appeal and confines this gem material to a very small place on the international market.

Sources

Jet is found in many localities, and it is often discovered as a by-product of coal mining. It is produced in Europe at a number of localities, in Spain, France, Germany, Poland and the USSR. However, the most famous place for jet is the town of Whitby, in Yorkshire, England. Deposits of jet can also be found in China, India, Turkey and in a number of states in the USA.

Treatment of Jet

Some fragile material (jet is very brittle) is resin-bonded to give it greater strength.

Synthetic Jet

True synthetic jet is not commercially manufactured.

Principal Gemstones that Can Simulate Jet

Virtually all gemstones that come in a black colour could be classed as potential jet simulants. Jet is relatively light in relation to its size, therefore the denser gemstones can be distinguished from this material.

The most deceptive imitations of jet are those made from plastics, resins, glasses and a black rubber-based material known as "vulcanite".

OTHER GEMSTONES

There are many minerals and other substances that are sometimes used as gem materials. It would be impractical to give details of them all here, but the collector and the jewellery buyer will occasionally be offered some of these during the course of their pursuits. A knowledge of the existence of these materials could be of benefit to them.

A number of local decorative stones are set in jewellery throughout the world. These can be well known locally, but rarely encountered elsewhere. Sometimes they are by-products of local ornamental stone industries producing items such as fireplaces and tabletops. Small amounts of gem-quality material are occasionally found among larger low-grade pieces, and these are utilized as curios in jewellery.

A few minerals form natural twinned cross-shaped crystals, and these were held in great esteem among the Christian religious communities. Some patterns seen in gem materials can have scenic or pictorial qualities. Other gem materials exhibit curious external forms in their natural state. Sometimes specialized local names are applied to these strange stones, belying their true nature and composition.

In the Middle Ages and the Renaissance period, great faith was placed in curious concretions that were found in the stomach of goats and sheep. These were known as *bezoars*, and were used to detect and dispel poisons by immersing them in suspect liquids. The possession of such a stone would no doubt discourage many poisoners, who ran an increased risk of being detected.

Meteorites come in a wide range of forms, and many beliefs have been associated with these objects of extraterrestrial origin. Some of these stones are made predominantly of a nickel-iron mixture, and

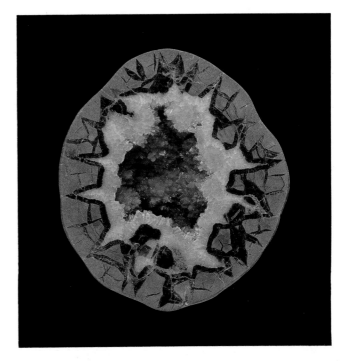

A Thunder Egg (septarion nodule) from Utah, U.S.A. Photograph courtesy of B.S. Lloyd of Gregory, Bottley & Lloyd.

microscopic diamonds are sometimes found in this type of meteorite. The other principal class is stony meteorites, which are made of a variety of minerals. All meteorites can contain very rare metal trace elements, which gives rise to considerable speculation regarding their origin. A meteorite is set in the wall of the Holy Shrine in Mecca, and is touched by thousands of pilgrims each year. This stone has been there for over 1000 years.

The horns, bones, hair and hooves of various animals have all been used at times in jewellery. Amulets and talismans are often made of strange mixtures of these materials. Some fossilized ammonites were thought to have fallen from the sky during thunderstorms, as they were uncovered by the erosive effects of wind and rain.

A list of other gem materials not otherwise detailed in this book is given below, in an attempt to illustrate to the reader the complexity, size and scope of the gemmological world.

The following gemstones are sometimes set in jewellery:

Andalusite	Gypsum	Rhodochrosite	Sphene (Titanite)
Apatite	Hematite	Rhodonite	Spodumene
Calcite	Idocrase	Scapolite	Steatite
Diopside	Iolite (cordierite)	Sinhalite	Verdite
Enstatite	Pyrite	Sodalite	Zoisite

The following gemstones are mainly cut for collectors and are rarely set in jewellery:

Actinolite	Cassiterite	Ekanite	Kyanite	Proustite	Saurolite
Amblygonite	Cerussite	Epidote	Lazulite	Purpurite	Stichtite
Anatase	Charoite	Euclase	Lazurite	Rhodizite	Taaffeite
Apophyllite	Chrysocolla	Fibrolite (Sillimanite)	Leucite	Rutile	Thomsonite
Augite	Colemanite	Granite (rock)	Magnesite	Sapphirine	Tremolite
Axinite	Crocoite	Hambergite	Meerschaum	Saussurite	Tugtupite
Azurite	Danburite	Hauyne	Natrolite	Scheelite	Variscite
Barite	Datolite	Hemimorphite	Petalite	Siderite	Vivianite
Benitoite	Dioptase	Howlite	Phenakite	Smaragdite	Willemite
Beryllonite	Dolomite	Hypersthene	Phosgenite	Smithsonite	Wulfenite
Brazilianite	Dumortierite	Kornerupine	Prehnite	Sphalerite	Zincite

NATURAL GLASSES

There are a number of forms of glass that occur in nature and that are used for gem material. The most common of these are the volcanic glasses known generally under the name of obsidian. This can be found in a variety of types and colours sometimes showing different coloured layers within one piece.

A dark smoky-brown transparent nodular form of obsidian from Arizona is sometimes known as "apache tears". There are also obsidians which have fine hair-like tubular inclusions which produce a "cat's-eye" effect when the material is in cabochons. One well-known decorative type of this gem is known as "snowflake obsidian", which is named after the white crystalline inclusions of cristobalite. These inclusions

A group of nineteenth-century models in glass of famous diamonds. These were made for exhibitions to show the size and cut of the original gems. Photograph courtesy of C. Cavey.

A range of paste/glass imitation gemstones demonstrating how deceptive these can be. Photograph courtesy of E.A. Jobbins.

The Renaissance gold, jewelled, and enamelled crown made for the Austro-Hungarian Emperor Rudolph II. The crown is set with an assortment of sapphires, table-cut diamonds, emeralds, red spinels, and natural pearls. Photograph courtesy of C. Cavey.

A group of black tektites, composed of natural glass of uncertain origin. Thailand. Photograph courtesy of C. Cavey.

have the appearance of white snow crystals on a black background.

In addition there are various peculiar natural glasses whose origins are uncertain. Natural glass nodules known as tektites are found in various areas of the world, and one current theory is that these were formed by the impact of huge meteorites upon the surface of the earth. The force of the impact is said to have been so great that these glass pieces were sent high into the atmosphere, to be moulded and etched as they fell back to the earth.

A transparent green etched tektite known as "moldavite" comes from areas in Czechoslovakia.

A strange form of transparent pale-straw-yellow glass is found in pieces weighing up to several pounds, in a wide area of the Libyan Desert. This material is

111

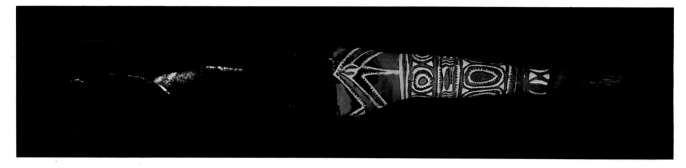

A black obsidian Aboriginal spearhead, used in Australia in the 19th century. Arrowheads, tools, etc., in natural glass are known from many parts of the world. Photograph courtesy of C. Cavey.

extremely pure and contains up to 95 per cent pure silica.

CHEMICAL COMPOSITION: variable, usually over 50 per cent Silica with various oxides.
COLOURS: almost all colours are possible, although as a general rule bright, distinct colours, other than black, are quite rare.
CRYSTAL SYSTEM: none.
HABIT: obsidians are found in large flow areas around extinct and active volcanic areas. Pieces are normally extracted by breaking the material up so that it can be easily transported. Tektites are normally quite small (very rarely up to fist size) and come in a wide variety of shapes.
HARDNESS: 5–6.
CUT: obsidians are often carved, tumbled, cabochoned, and occasionally faceted. Tektites are sometimes cut for collectors but are usually more interesting in their natural state.

History

Obsidian is a material which has been used for the manufacture of arrow- and spear-heads by primitive cultures. Mirrors and votive objects, and razor-sharp sacrificial knife blades were made of obsidian by many of the Pre-Columbian civilizations in the Americas.

In Thailand tektites were worn for many centuries as protection against the evil eye. The curious shapes in which these sometimes form have given rise to a range of specific beliefs relating directly to the shape of the stones.

Sources

Obsidian is found in many areas throughout the globe. There are a large number of sources in the USA,

Mexico, Iceland, Japan and the USSR, all producing a range of this material.

Tektites are found in abundance along a belt which runs across Thailand, Indo-China, and all the way to Australia. They are also found in lesser quantities in other parts of the world. The only known source of green transparent tektites (moldavites) is the deposits of Czechoslovakia.

Small glass beads resembling tektites were found among rock samples taken during the American moon missions of the 1970s.

Treatment of Glasses

Natural glass can be subject to remelting.

Synthetic Glasses

Many types of glass are produced for a wide range of industrial applications, and as simulants of other gemstones.

Principal Gemstones that Can Simulate Natural Glasses

Natural glasses are most closely simulated by manmade glasses, although many gemstones can sometimes be mistaken for these materials, including jasper.

PRECIOUS METALS

The undisputed king of precious metals has to be gold. The name is derived from its yellow colour and it is the one metal above all others that is directly associated with the sun and its virtues.

Silver has been held in high esteem since early antiquity. The name is derived from the colour of the metal, and it has been the one metal associated directly with the moon, and with the beliefs and virtues associated with this planet.

Platinum is a metal that has been known for thousands of years, but was not officially discovered until 1735. For many years it was regarded as a nuisance, and was discarded during gold-panning. It was not until the late nineteenth century that the technology was available to allow the metal to be smelted and worked. The name was derived from *platina*, or silver, in reference to its colour.

CHEMICAL COMPOSITION: gold, silver and platinum are all pure elements.
COLOURS: gold is alloyed with other metals to make it harder and more suitable for use in jewellery. Depending on the metals used gold will have an underlying tone of colour. White, green, red, blue, violet, and black gold are all produced for specialist design purposes in jew-
ellery-making. Silver is a white silver colour, and platinum is a steely-white colour, greyer than silver.
CRYSTAL SYSTEM: for all three, cubic.
HABIT: gold is found as nuggets, in seams, and sometimes as small dispersed particles in a rock. In the large modern

Fob seal in 22 carat gold and inlaid in multi-coloured enamel with and engraved armorial amethyst, circa 1750. Photograph courtesy of C. Cavey.

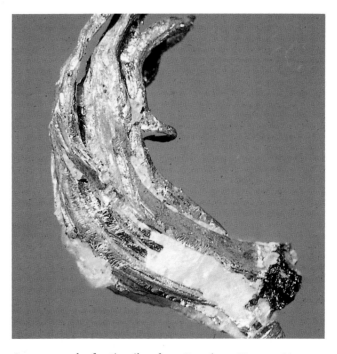

A rare example of native silver from Kongsberg, Norway. Most silver is mined from mineral compounds containing this metal. Photograph courtesy of E.A. Jobbins.

mines gold-bearing rocks are crushed to extract the gold content. On average it can take several tons of ore to yield one ounce of gold. Gold, unlike silver, is usually found native and rarely as a compound. It is sometimes mined in magnificent sharp arborescent (tree-like) crystal groups.

Silver is mainly produced as a by-product from lead-mining, and is principally found in compound minerals which contain other metals, such as antimony, arsenic, sulphur, copper, lead and zinc. When silver occurs as a native metal it can form arborescent crystal groups and strange-shaped wires.

Platinum is by far the rarest of the three metals, and is mainly mined from ores containing small quantities of the metal. Occasionally platinum can be found as nuggets, although these are rarely ever over one ounce in size.
HARDNESS: pure gold and pure silver, 2.5–3.0; pure platinum, 4–5.

History

In nearly all ancient cultures gold was revered above all other metals. It was probably the ability of the pure metal to resist most acids and tarnishing that gained it this premier position. Many recently excavated items made in gold alloys are covered with corrosion from the base metal elements they contain. Very pure gold items, however, survive perfectly, and many have been found untouched by the rigours of time.

Gold had, and still has, a deep religious significance, symbolizing the solar force and its life-generating character. This metal has been used to make some of the most important and valuable objects known to man. Gold medals still symbolize the height of achievement, and gold wedding rings are worn by a large proportion of the peoples of the globe. Gold is used in medicines, particularly for the eyes, and is taken in flakes in the belief that it will improve the overall health of the body.

Gold is not only used to make decorative objects,

A Mogul Indian rock crystal bottle with rubies and emeralds set in gold. 17th Century. Photograph courtesy of E.A. Jobbins.

A group of Ancient Greek and Etruscan gold jewellery illustrating their range of styles and forms. Photograph courtesy of C. Cavey.

coins and jewellery, but is now extensively employed in modern micro-electrical components, because of its ability to conduct electricity efficiently.

Silver has been used since the dawn of time as the secondary metal to gold. It was used in symbolism to represent all the forces and influence of the moon. Silver, unlike gold, readily oxidizes in the atmosphere. A black silver oxide layer will form quite quickly on any object made of this metal. A thin gold layer is frequently applied to silver objects, by plating or coating, and these are then described as silver gilt. This process is normally applied to any silver objects likely to come into contact with acidic liquids which will instantly discolour unprotected silverware.

Silver has been used in coinage, household items, and in jewellery since the beginnings of civilization. It is a far more common metal than gold and was therefore more freely available.

Silver is now generally used for low-cost jewellery, although many fine designers have used it in prefer-ence to gold. Diamonds were usually set in this metal,

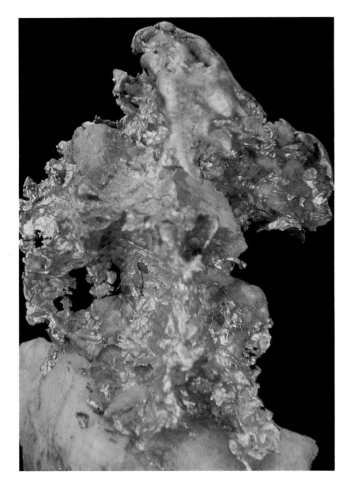

A piece of milky quartz, intergrown with native gold, from Sonora, Mexico. Most gold is mined from material that yields only one ounce of gold for every ten tons of ore. Photograph courtesy of E.A. Jobbins.

tries, Australia, South America, and the USSR.

Silver is mined in many locations throughout the world, including Germany, Chile, Mexico, Peru, Bolivia, and a number of locations in the USA and the USSR. The finest native silver is found at Konsberg in Norway.

Platinum is found at relatively few localities. The principal mining areas are in South Africa, Canada, Alaska, the USSR, Australia, and a number of South American countries.

Treatment of Precious Metals

Gold is normally used in an alloyed form and the carat is determined by the proportion of the pure metal present in its make-up. The use of carats dates back to the time of the Roman Empire. The principal gold coin of the empire was the *aureus*, which weighed 24 carats if it was made of pure gold. During various inflationary periods these coins were made of gold with added

A 19th century copy of a gold pendant based on an ancient Greek original, made in Rome by A. Castellani. Photograph courtesy of C. Cavey.

as the whiteness of it would complement the colour of the stone. Poorly coloured diamonds may appear to be of an inferior colour if set in gold.

Silver compounds are used in a variety of industrial, medicinal and chemical processes.

Platinum has only been used in jewellery during the last hundred years. It is much harder to work and proportionately heavier than gold. This is why pieces of jewellery made in this metal normally cost considerably more than equivalent items in white gold. Rings have been known to be carved from solid nuggets of platinum, prior to the discovery of the ability to work this hard metal.

Sources

Gold is found in large deposits in a number of states of the USA, South Africa and many other African coun-

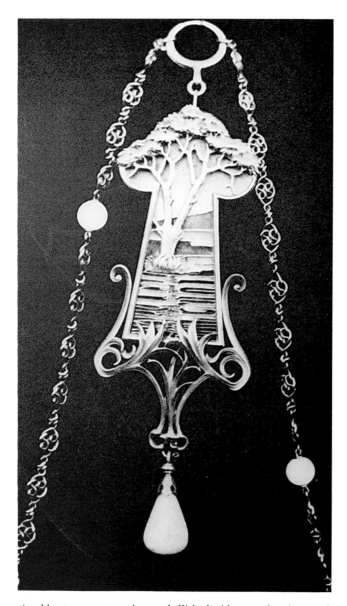

A gold bracelet in the form of a double headed snake. Ancient Roman. Photograph courtesy of C. Cavey.

A gold art nouveau pendant embellished with enamel and natural pearls, designed by G. Fouquet. Circa 1900. Photograph courtesy of C. Cavey.

copper and other base metals, and the weight of the coin was therefore proportionately less. Hence, today, we still use the term 24 carat to describe pure gold. Many items of ancient Greek jewellery were made from a silver and gold mixture, known as electrum. These were probably made from nuggets of gold that had a naturally high silver content.

Today gold used in jewellery varies in percentage from 22 carat, which is over 90 per cent pure, down to 9 carat, which only has to contain 37.5 per cent pure gold. White gold is an alloy of gold with a percentage of palladium or nickel. Palladium white gold is whiter than nickel white gold, and both are usually plated with the hard platinum-related metal, rhodium.

Silver is used in two purities in the United Kingdom. These are Britannia Standard, which is at least 95 per cent pure silver, and Sterling, which is at least 92.5 per cent pure silver. In other countries percentages as low as 80 per cent pure silver are acceptable.

Platinum is usually used in a very pure form and to bear a British hallmark for the metal it must be 95 per cent pure.

Principal Gemstones that Can Simulate Precious Metals

COPPER-BASED ALLOYS: there are many that make convincing simulants of gold.

MANY WHITE METAL ALLOYS: can be confused with silver and platinum. In the year 1347, hallmarking was introduced on precious metals in London for the very purpose of protecting the purchasers of precious metal items. Hallmarking is now standard practice in a number of countries, but all have their own systems and marks. The reader is advised to study books specifically on this subject to gain further information.

A great many items of antique jewellery bear no hallmarks. It was the practice in the past not to hallmark many items of gem-set jewellery, on the premise that the value of the gems far exceeded that of the metal. Items can be submitted for testing and their metal content assessed by valuers, so that they can be hallmarked with current marks if the owner so desires.

CARVED AND ENGRAVED GEMS

As we have seen in the earlier sections of this book, gemstones have been used by mankind since the dawn of history. The carving and engraving of gem materials is known as far back as the civilizations of ancient Egypt and ancient China.

Gem materials are hard and difficult to work, and softer stones seem to have been preferred in the earlier periods. Man's ability to work hard stone materials dates back to the Stone Age. The name of this period in evolutionary history is derived from the stone tools which were produced at that time. These tools were usually made of flint, which is an impure form of chalcedony. Arrow-heads, scrapers, spear-points, and hand axes were generally made by the skilful chipping of one flint against another. It remains a mystery at which point the ability actually to cut stones was discovered. It is well known, however, that cut stone axe-heads exist that have been ground by abrasion into the desired shape, and some of these date back to the late Stone Age period.

It is quite easy to cut or grind a softer stone with the powder from a hard stone, if it is placed on a suitable surface and a liquid is applied to reduce friction. The harder the powdered stone in relation to the softer one, the quicker and easier it is to cut. The favourite hard stone of the ancient cutters was emery, an impure form of the mineral corundum (the gem varieties of which are ruby and sapphire). The ability to cut stones as hard as 7 on Mohs' scale was certainly known in ancient Egypt, Babylon, India and China. Many of the large stone carvings left by the ancient Egyptians were made from granite rock. The main

Two cylinder seals of Babylonian origin, made of blue chalcedony and green serpentine. Dating from 2500 B.C. to 700 B.C. Photograph courtesy of C. Cavey.

117

constituent minerals of granite are quartz, mica and feldspar, so that the ability to work quartz gem materials, even on a large scale, existed at this period.

There are three basic forms which carvings can take, and they are usually summarized in the following way. Carvings in the round are three-dimensional, and have the basic form of the subject copied. Cameo carvings are normally cut in a stone and are flat in relief on the surface. The better examples utilize different coloured layers in the material to emphasize details of the various subject matters. The background is usually cut away in these stones so that the design stands out from the surrounding stone. Carvings in intaglio are cut into the stone, and are usually in reverse, so that wax impressions taken from them can be used for making seals.

Carvings in the round were favoured for larger decorative objects, and less commonly seen in jewellery of any period. Carvings in cameo were very popular in jewellery and formed an important part of

A Greco-Roman carnelian. The God Apollo is standing in the foreground with two attendants. Photograph courtesy of C. Cavey.

Below: Sassanion seals of the type designed for suspension from a cord, circa 5th century. Photograph courtesy of C. Cavey.

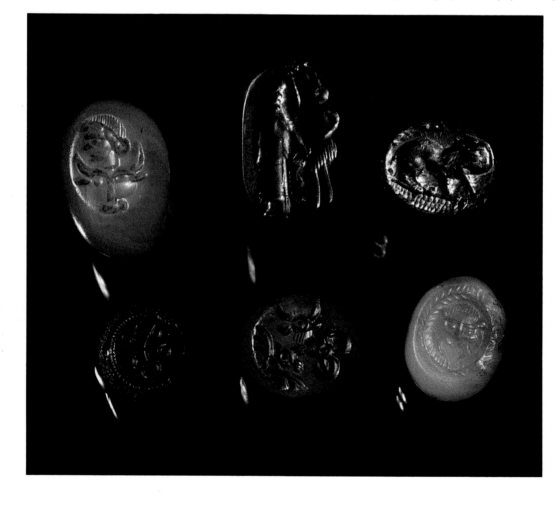

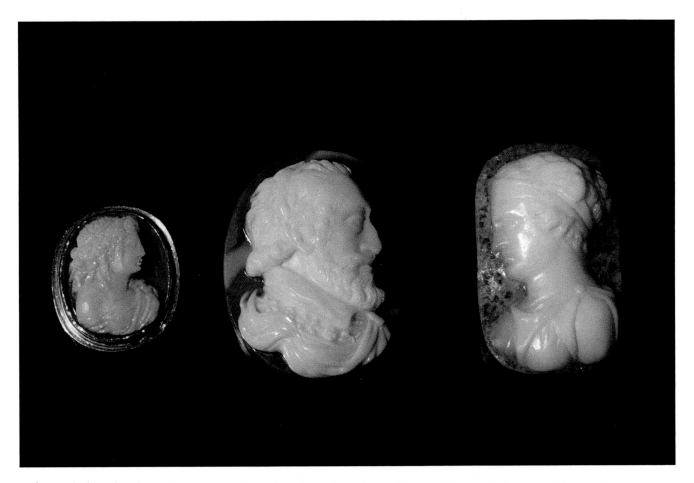

male and female dress in the ancient Greek and Roman civilizations. Cameos are fashionable periodically, and have been utilized in many jewels right up to the present day. Carvings in intaglio are the most common; these can exhibit remarkable detail, and have a principal function other than decoration. The sealing of documents was effected by making an impression of the gem in a little clay or melted wax. The chief means of identification, and the authority of a person, was carried by the impressions from these stones.

There are many Biblical references to engraved gems. Apart from the engraved stone tablets brought down by Moses from Mount Sinai, all twelve gems set in the breastplate of the Jewish High Priest were engraved with the names of the twelve tribes of Israel. The authority of kings and nobles was conveyed by documents that bore their seals, and many of these were carved in gem materials.

Carved gemstones have survived in far greater numbers from ancient civilizations than almost any other form of sculpture or art form. Intaglios are the most common of the surviving engraved gems, probably because of their use as personal seals, which

Henry IV, King of France, in the centre with two other late Renaissance cameos. Photograph courtesy of C. Cavey.

would consequently be buried with their owners. These come in a wide range of shapes and forms.

The ancient Egyptians favoured seals made in the form of the scarab beetle, the inscription or device being engraved on the flat underbelly. Many scarabs were not used as seals but were purely talismanic devices, others were just decorative and bore no inscription. Full in-the-round carving was quite common in this period and many of the gods and goddesses were rendered in brightly coloured jaspers. True cameos were not known in the early kingdoms, and they were introduced into Egypt by Alexander the Great. The Greeks probably adopted the scarab form of seal as a result of Egyptian influence.

The ancient Babylonian Empire most commonly used a completely different form of seal. These consisted of a cylinder which was drilled down its length with a series of pictures and sometimes script engraved on its outer surface. The seals were thought to have been carried on a cord round the wrist. They were used for sealing by rolling them over wet clay to make

119

an impression. Some of them date to as early as 2500 BC, but they remained in production up to about 700 BC. These stones can make impressions of considerable length, as they will effectively print a continuous design. They appear to have been used for sealing containers, and even the doors of houses, in addition to documents. Babylonians leaving their houses for the day would seal their front doors with an impressed piece of wet clay (door locks were not used).

The Assyrians used many seals made in an elongated flattened conical form. These normally had an oval base which was engraved with a suitable scene or device. The Minoan culture of Crete used round seal stones which frequently had two concave surfaces, one for engraving, the other forming the rear of the stone.

A microscopically etched carnelian, only one inch across engraved with the 99 names of god and 2 verses of the Koran. Dated 1754. Probably of Arabic origin. Photograph courtesy of C. Cavey.

Cameo portrait of Pericles. 17th century with a later mount. Photograph courtesy of C. Cavey.

The Greeks and Etruscans both adopted scaraboid forms of seal, but as time went by this design degenerated and was eventually replaced by engraved but undecorated stones. Most of the early Greek and Etruscan gems had the seal design surrounded by a border, which took various forms and styles.

By the time the Roman Empire dominated Europe, the art of gem-engraving had reached its height, and engraved gems were not only worn but collected by many of the prominent personages of the day. Julius Caesar is said to have deposited five chests full of engraved gems for safekeeping in the Temple of the Vestal Virgins. There is some debate among scholars as to the precise period that gem-engraving reached its peak. Certainly, there are some very finely engraved

Greek and Roman gems. Judging the best of these, however, remains purely a matter of personal taste.

Ancient intaglios were normally rather small, and were rarely made over one inch in diameter during the Roman Empire. Greek gems tend to be even smaller, no doubt for convenience in wearing. Cameos were sometimes carved in microscopic sizes, and in extraordinary detail, but they were also made in large sizes to form decorative bowls, dishes and cups. A number of fine large cameos exist in many of the world's gem collections, and some of these date back to the Greco-Roman period.

There is a truly exceptional sapphire cameo preserved in the Fitzwilliam Museum, Cambridge, England. This stone measures over one and three-quarter inches in one direction, and has been dated stylistically to the first century BC. Carved sapphires were not at all common in the ancient world, and many more intag-

Opposite: *A group of four tools, three of which are carved into animal forms, all of which were used by Alfred L. Pocock for carving, shaping and fine-finishing his carvings. Careful examination of the animal heads will reveal diamond and sapphire points set into these tools. Photograph courtesy of Mrs. W. Bottley.*

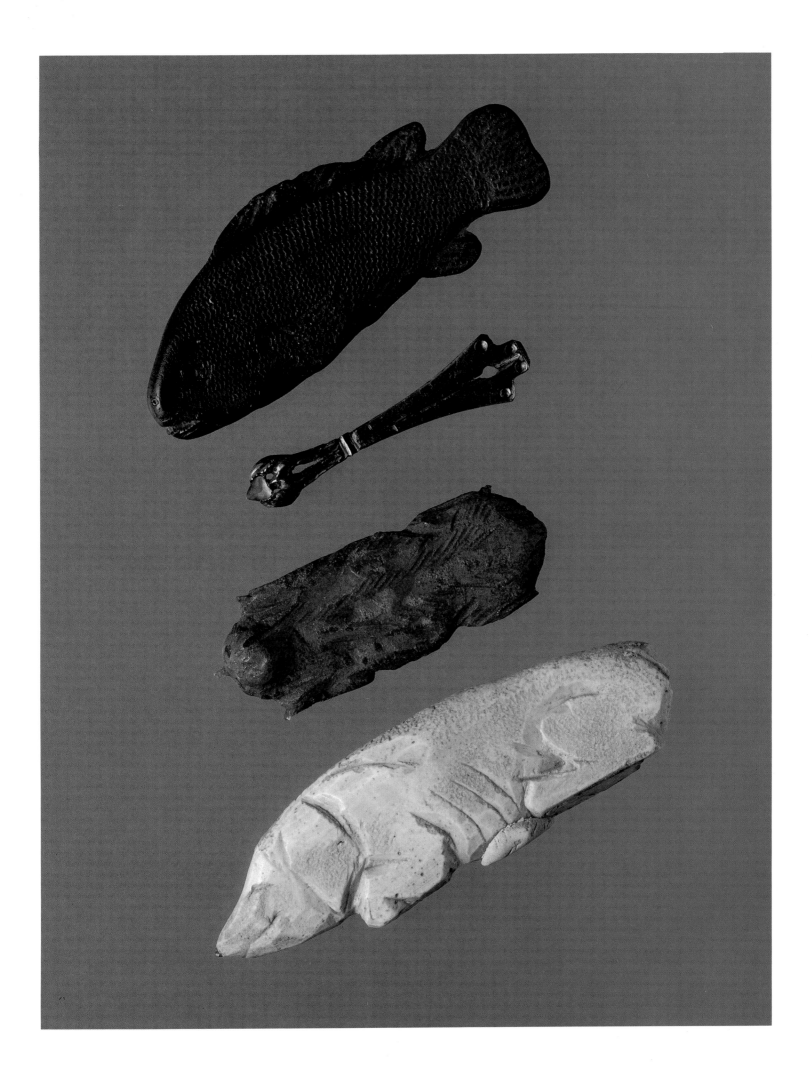

lios survive than cameos. Powdered diamond and diamond-tipped tools must have been used in the execution of these gems, and they are normally quite small (rarely exceeding half an inch across).

The bulk of ancient engraving was carried out on varieties of the mineral chalcedony, and more rarely on the harder stones, such as beryl. Many softer stones were worked, including a number of the varieties of serpentine and marble. Lapis-lazuli was used but not greatly favoured except in the eastern provinces, although a number of classical examples still exist of engraving on this gem. True emerald was very scarce at this period and the bulk of the material was of a rather poor quality. Most of the finely engraved classical gems which have been described as emeralds have on close examination proved to be an emerald-green chrome-coloured chalcedony. Peridot, amazonite, garnet, amethyst, citrine, rock crystal, prase and hematite were all in use. A number of high-quality convincing glass copies imitating gems were made as a cheaper substitute for gemstones, and many of these survive today.

After the fall of the Roman Empire, the art of

A group of cameos showing a range of styles. From left to right: 18th, 19th and 17th century. Photograph courtesy of C. Cavey.

carving and engraving gems virtually died out. In the early medieval period some jewellery was made containing engraved gemstones, but these were normally older classical stones that were remounted. At the same time a curious transition was taking place as Christianity developed. Many Greek and Roman gems had been utilized in religious objects and rings, and a number bore engraved symbols representing the gods. A complete reinterpretation of the subject-matter now allowed Athena to become the Virgin Mary, Zeus to become God the Father, and so on.

There were some attempts at gem-engraving during these transitional periods, but the results were usually of poor quality compared with classical examples. The Byzantine Empire produced a range of engraved plates on rock crystal, and on heliotrope (bloodstone), most of which were of a religious or secular nature. Superb garnet inlay work was used in jewellery in northern Europe during this period, and fine thin plates of garnet were cut in stepped shapes and overlaid on to

122

A portrait of Emperor Septimus Servus cut in the 18th century in an attempt to emulate the style of Greco-Roman work. Contemporary mount. Photograph courtesy of C. Cavey.

Portrait of the God Pan on a sard signed with a spurious Greek signature. Probably made by the Pickler workshops in the late 18th century. Photograph courtesy of C. Cavey.

Roman Republican period jasper seal depicting a lion eating a deer, with a vulture looking on. Re-set in the 19th century. Photograph courtesy of C. Cavey.

Two carnelian seal stones. The orange stone is a 19th-century copy based on classical design of the whitish stone which has changed colour after being burnt in a fire. Photograph courtesy of C. Cavey.

impressed gold foils (as, for example, in the finds from the Sutton Hoo ship burial, now in the British Museum).

A revival of the gem-engraver's art took place during the early Renaissance period, when a profound interest was being expressed in all forms of classical art. A number of poorly engraved classical gems were reworked, and there was a good profit to be made in selling modern work as genuine classical material to the unsuspecting collector. An immense quantity of fine work was produced at this period and carried out

on an enormous range of gem materials. Large cameos were back in production and the Medicis, who had one of the greatest collections of classical art, sponsored the great craftsmen of the day to produce jewels, cameos and assorted *objets d'art* in a variety of gem materials.

It was certainly normal practice by the Elizabethan period to present honoured subjects with suitably set cameo portraits, as tokens of appreciation and loyalty. By the seventeenth century it had become common for monarchs, noblemen and the gentry to collect

123

Aetatis Suæ 52. An° 1601

Gorlæus hîc in ære scalptus, æs cui,
Argentum, & aurum, Roma quod vel Græcia
Signauit vnquam, gemmaque & carus lapis
Olim vetustis destinatus annulis
Perennitatis gratiam debent suæ.
Nunc experitur an Metalla a sæculis
Qui vindicata sæculo nostro dedit,
Ipsum futuris dent Metalla sæculis.

H. Grot.

classical antiquities. The market for antique cameos and intaglios was never more vigorous. In the eighteenth century there was considerable competition between the wealthy houses of Europe as to who owned the best collections of classical gems. This gave rise to an enormous number of engravers producing copies of classical work. The Russian Empress Catherine the Great spent considerable sums on acquiring engraved gems, and had all the major collections of the day copied in glass replicas by the Scotsman James Tassie (he produced over 15,000 different replicas). Indeed, these glass reproduction gems are now referred to in the trade as "Tassies".

There were many gems engraved with subjects loosely based on classical works. The most notable perpetrator of this deception was the nephew of the King of Poland, Prince Poniatowsky. He inherited a collection of several hundred genuine classical gems from his father. He then employed a number of engravers of the day to produce a enormous collection (over 5000) of large engraved gems. These covered an immense range of subject-matter, and all were signed in Greek with known or spurious classical artists' signatures. The attempt to pass this collection off as genuine classical material virtually destroyed the market in engraved gems in the first part of the nineteenth century. Certain collectors were known to have paid as much as 1000 guineas (100 guineas a year was a reasonable income) for one fine classical gem.

Many fine works in cameo and intaglio were carried

Opposite: A portrait of Abraham Gorlaeus, with his collection of engraved gems and gem-set rings. Note the trays of loose gems, designed carefully to fit into book frames, which are used to store his collection. Taken from his book, which was the first published on this subject in 1601. Photograph courtesy of C. Cavey.

An engraved plate showing an enormous classical cameo (6 × 5 inches) of the Roman Emperor Claudius and his family. Published in Vienna, 1788. Photograph courtesy of C. Cavey.

Grandeur naturelle.

L'EMPEREUR CLAUDE et sa Famille.

ΤΡΥΦΩΝ
ΕΠΟΙΕΙ

Gemmæ
magnitudo.

NVPTIÆ·CVPID·ET·PSYCHES·
TRYPHONIS·OPVS
Ex Sardonych. Anaglyph. exscalptum.
In Dactyliotheca Arundelliana Londini.

out during the eighteenth century, and some of these can be bought on the current market for a fraction of their original equivalent cost when they were made. In rare cases the artist was of sufficient note in his day to sign the gems with his own name.

There were over 900 catalogued engravers working on these gems between the seventeenth and nineteenth centuries. Only one English engraver was recognized in his day as a true artist by his admission to the Royal Academy of Arts in London; his name was Edmund Burch. A pupil of Burch, Nathaniel Marchant, was to become the most famous English engraver of his day and could charge immense sums, sometimes up to 500 guineas, for one intaglio.

In the latter part of the nineteenth century many gems were commercially engraved but few could compare with the quality of eighteenth-century workmanship. Cameos were very popular in a wide range of jewellery at this time, and it was fashionable for a while to use shell cameos for such purposes. These were principally cut in areas around Naples in southern Italy. (Shell cameos had been used in jewellery since the sixteenth century.) They were much easier to produce than stone cameos, as they were cut with hand-held sharpened steel tools, and simple examples could be made in a few hours.

Carving *objets d'art* in gem materials was certainly fashionable during the Renaissance, and there was a revived interest in this form of decoration in the nineteenth century. Many finely worked bowls, cups, dishes and other decorative objects in the Renaissance style were made in Austria during this period. Some of these are of such fine quality and detail that they have been mistaken for earlier pieces.

The dating of engraved gems is a very difficult matter, and it is virtually impossible to ascribe accurate dates to the majority of material. Craftsmen of later centuries who understood the techniques employed by earlier engravers have produced almost perfect copies. Several factors can be used as a helpful guide. Classical cameos are normally of more than one colour, flattish and engraved in a stiff style. They may be very large or very small, and the detail may be excellent to poor, depending on the period and the craftsman. Intaglios in the classical period were nor-

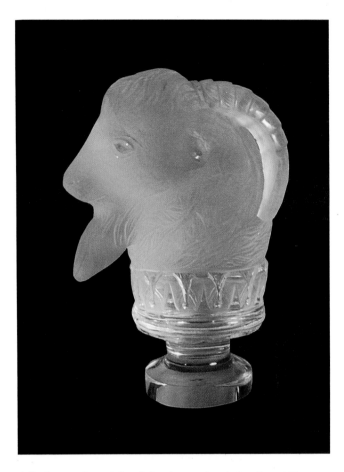

A finely carved goat's headed rock crystal seal. Russian, 19th century. Photograph courtesy of C. Cavey.

mally under one inch in diameter, and the design filled the bulk of the area designated for sealing on the gem. Later examples lack these qualities. The method used to suggest hair on portraits, in particular, offers a good guide when trying to determine the differences in techniques in the various periods of history.

By the late nineteenth century, a Russian by the name of Peter Carl Fabergé had an enormous workshop which produced a wide range of hand-cut and carved gem materials. He employed many craftsmen from all over Europe, and most of the work was carried out in the city of St Petersburg. Several of his worksmasters were of foreign extraction and came from Sweden, Finland, Switzerland, and Germany. Fabergé workshops made an extraordinary range of items, including a number of carvings made of gem materials. Many books have been written about Fabergé's life and skills, and the materials sold in his various shops.

Fabergé opened a shop in London, which was run

Opposite: *An engraving representing a cameo of "the marriage of Cupid and Psyche", which was then in the collection of the Dukes of Norfolk, at Arundel. This is taken from a book by M.P. de Stosch, written in 1724, which promoted a great interest in artists' signatures found on ancient engraved gems. Photograph courtesy of C. Cavey.*

Opposite: *Finely carved stylized head in chrysoprase, executed by Alfred L. Pocock in the 1960s. Photograph courtesy of Mrs W. Bottley.*

An engraving representing three classical gems from the collections in the Florence Museum, published by A. Gorri in 1732. Photograph courtesy of C. Cavey.

by a Mr H.C. Bainbridge. He was approached by Queen Alexandra to have Fabergé provide some wax models of two of her animals which she wished him to carve in gem materials. In view of the distance between London and St Petersburg it was necessary to find a local person capable of carrying out this work. After consulting the Royal Academy Schools, H.C. Bainbridge was referred to a scholarship pupil by the name of Alfred Lyndhurst Pocock. This young man had impressed his tutors with his diverse artistic abilities. Pocock was born on Christmas Eve 1881, and

was the son of two accomplished painters. His mother and his father had both won Rome scholarships, and they painted there before moving to North London.

Pocock made the models in wax, and these were subsequently sent to Russia for executing in stone. It was not long after this encounter that Pocock showed Bainbridge a couple of carvings that he had created himself in some hard gem materials, which he had found as beach pebbles. It would appear from his account of this matter that Bainbridge took it upon himself to offer these carvings to the Queen, without

reference to Fabergé in Russia.

The carvings were duly purchased by the Queen, who was delighted with the work, and a regular relationship was formed. It is hard to establish whether this became an official or informal arrangement, but Pocock certainly took on many commissions from the Queen and H.C. Bainbridge, via Fabergé's London shop, and executed a considerable number of carvings. The style of his work varied considerably, as he was capable of emulating almost any technique known to produce a desired effect or form, and, unlike the highly polished carvings made in Fabergé's St Petersburg workshops, he used a wide range of polishing methods and finishes.

Pocock's early life had been totally influenced by the love and devotion of both his parents to art, and although he did not excel academically at school, his exceptional artwork won him a scholarship and silver medal at Regent Street Polytechnic. He subsequently won another scholarship which took him to the Royal Academy School.

He gained the nickname "Bones" whilst at the Royal

A magnificent carved chalcedony rhinoceros, 10 inches in length. The detail of the skin texture, and the movement captured in this carving, clearly demonstrate the skill and artistry present in the work of G. Dreher. Photograph courtesy of G. Dreher.

Opposite: *A gorilla carved from a single block of obsidian (natural volcanic glass). Carved by G. Dreher. Photograph courtesy of G. Dreher.*

Academy School, due to his amazing ability to portray so realistically the bones and musculature of animals in works of art. He was employed as a student to work on the stone sculpture of the Queen Victoria Memorial, which now stands outside Buckingham Palace, and he went on to assist the British Museum (Natural History) in reconstructions and casts of the skulls and bones of prehistoric man.

After his discovery by H.C. Bainbridge, Pocock's time and efforts were totally taken up with innumerable commissions from Fabergé's London shop. A large part of the royal family's collection of Fabergé animals, many of which were Pocock's work, is now housed at Sandringham, Norfolk. The commission

work for wax models, drawings and finished products, kept Pocock busy until 1914, when he was drafted into the army. Sadly, Fabergés shops, craftsmen and workshops all suffered during the Great War and, with the subsequent Russian Revolution, the workforce was disbanded and the business closed.

Pocock returned to carving after the war, and formed a relationship with James Gregory, a well-known mineralogist of the day, who sold him an assortment of rough materials for carving. In 1931, Gregory retired, selling his business to Mr and Mrs E.P.

G. Dreher working on the fine detail of a carved bison in brown obsidian. The carving and engraving tools he uses in this picture have remained unchanged for over two hundred years. Photograph courtesy of G. Dreher.

Opposite: *A chimpanzee carved in two-colour obsidian, showing the clever use of this material. Carved by G. Dreher. Photograph courtesy of G. Dreher.*

Bottley. The relationship that Pocock enjoyed with Gregory gained momentum, as a result of the constructive attitude taken by the Bottleys to Pocock's

An extraordinary carving of an orang-utan, executed in an exceptional block of red jasper by G. Dreher. Photograph courtesy of G. Dreher.

skills and work. This relationship developed into a life-long friendship, and considerably broadened the scope and range of materials he was able to employ.

Unlike many artists, Alfred Pocock could work in almost any medium — drawing, painting, etching, carving in relief, in cameo and intaglio, and in the round. He had a truly amazing ability to capture the essence of living creatures and to express their nature and character fluidly in the cold, unforgiving medium of gem material. He made many diverse carvings, paintings, models, and casts. He would study rough pieces of gem material for months, seeking inspiration from their natural shape. Sometimes he would take a

134

plaster cast of the rough stone and carefully work it, to see if a prospective design would be successful.

Pocock studied many techniques, and was an unequalled master of carving scenes, figures and animals, *inside* amber, working with his tools through a tiny slit in the back of the piece (see illustration "Birth of the Fairies"). He studied in Paris a skill then known as the "French Technique". A design was painted on to a chalcedony in a paste made of a mixture of lead oxide and other compounds. The stone was then fired in a low temperature furnace, and the design became part of its surface. This technique was used in the Middle East to decorate beads over 2000 years ago.

Almost any material inspired Pocock's imagination. He resorted to carving redundant black ebony piano keys during the war, to keep in practice. He even carved many of his tools into the form of animals, and had sharp sapphire and diamond fragments set into these at convenient points on their protruding surface.

G. Dreher working on "roughing out" a piece of smoky quartz, prior to detailed carving, at his workshop in Idar-Oberstein, West Germany. Photograph courtesy of G. Dreher.

His carving always took full account of the natural marking and contours of the material he was working, often incorporating in his designs the natural etch marks, pits and cavities present in rough gems. He would normally use the minimum of carving he considered necessary to convey the nature and character of the subject he was portraying.

Pocock produced over 200 carvings in the years between 1905 and 1914, and most of these were commissioned through Fabergé's London shop. The total volume of his work is not recorded, but it is known he made over 100 pieces for Mr and Mrs Bottley during the course of his career, which ended with his death in the late 1960s. He signed and dated many of his later works, but none of his carvings made

A peregrine falcon in a variety of gem materials, and then cleverly assembled and mounted on a natural mineral base. The work of G. Dreher. Photograph courtesy of G. Dreher.

for Fabergé bear any signature. Of the many pieces of his work that have disappeared into private collections, there are several that deserve to be mentioned here. Pocock made, by special commission, an entire Noah's Ark in precious metal and gemstones, with innumerable carved animals that were added to over a period of several years. One superb Red Indian head made of fine matrix opal is now in the permanent display in the jewellery gallery at the Victoria and Albert Museum, London.

Jade Carving

The carving of gemstones in China dates back to the neolithic period. The most popular material worked was the nephrite variety of jade. There are no recorded ancient deposits of this material within China and it is thought that all of this material had to be imported.

The oldest jade carvings certainly reflect this view, as they are normally small and in many cases no more than thin slices of jade that are worked into a variety of shapes. Gradually the style of carving developed and, as more material became available.

Within the last fifty years two jade burial suits composed of green nephrite plates, which are pierced at the edges and threaded together with gold wires, were discovered. These date back to the second century BC. Entire sarcophagi (coffins) exist that have been painstakingly hollowed out of this extremely tough material.

The style of carving varies to some extent with period, although the Chinese had a habit of copying earlier forms and designs, a practice they have continued right up till the present day. There are a number of jade carvings illustrated in this work, and these try to show the progression, development of style, form, and techniques as the age pass. The history and development of Chinese jade carving is a complex subject and the reader is referred to specialist books on this subject for further information.

The other principal jade-carving civilizations of Central and South America developed in a similar way to the Chinese. The carvings of the earlier Chinese periods can easily be mistaken for Pre-Columbian material, as they are very similar in style and form. One easy way to distinguish these is to identify the gem material. Early Chinese jades are always made of nephrite, Pre-Columbian jades of jadeite.

Pre-Columbian jade carvings are often finished with an incredibly high polish, and little is known of the techniques employed to produce this. Many other materials were worked and carved by these cultures, one of the favourites being turquoise. There are several examples of human skulls overlaid with cut interlocking plates of this gem material. Many skilful hours of work went into the production of these articles, and it is a great tragedy that no records survive of the lapidary techniques.

The practice of carving and engraving gems in the modern world is by no means dead. There are two main world centres of commercial gem-carving, in Hong Kong and Idar-Oberstein, in West Germany. The modern carvings from Hong Kong range from jewellery pieces made in a number of gem materials, and in a wide range of qualities, to superb modern carvings in fine jade and other hard stones.

In Idar-Oberstein an immense and diverse range of high-quality carvings is produced. There are numerous families that have been cutting and carving gems for many generations, and some can trace their histories back over 300 years. There are also a number of cameo cutters who specialize in this art. One of the outstanding craftsmen in this area is Richard Haan.

The German lapidary industry produces a wide

Ancient Greek intaglio seal, in the form of a scarab. Its base is microscopically engraved with the chained Prometheus, having his liver eaten by a bird. The gold mount is of 19th-century workmanship. Photograph courtesy of C. Cavey.

range of cut and carved gem materials. There are many good carvers, but there is one truly prominent artist, whose work exceeds all others in detail and manufacture: Gerd Dreher.

The Dreher family have been carving and working gem materials in Idar-Oberstein for five generations. The tradition started with Karl Dreher (1861–1943), who then passed his skill and knowledge down to his son Hermann Dreher (1886–1960). Apart from producing items for the local market, he was specially commissioned through a contact in Idar-Oberstein to carve for Fabergé. Herman's son Paul (1910–1968) was also trained as a carver and produced a wide range of excellent animal carvings in his own workshop. He went on to develop an excellent reputation as one of the finest carvers of his day.

Gerd Dreher was brought up in the family tradition and served for three and a half years as an apprentice carver. After he graduated he went on to study development of design and the art of oil painting. During this period his work was acknowledged when he gained two awards. In the early stages of his career, he made many carvings for customers, copying a number of famous items from museums, learning by this experience the delicate skills of finely detailed carving. He also acquired the technique known commonly as "pietra dura". This involves the precise carving and inlaying of a series of different coloured stones into a background (usually black marble), in order to create pictorial scenes and portraits.

Unlike many other carvers, Dreher was not happy with merely copying other people's works. He gradually developed a style that could accurately emulate animals, birds, and plants, not only in their static positions but also in full movement. The amazing, naturalistic facial expressions that he attains in his carvings can only be compared with the live animals themselves. He spends many painstaking hours studying numerous books and photographs, and frequently makes and studies video films of his potential subjects. He also leaves his workshop to observe animals and birds in their natural habitats in the local forests before he commits himself to execute a carving. Sometimes he has found it necessary to purchase small rodents, such as mice and hamsters, to study in detail at close quarters before he has immortalized them in gem material.

Dreher has developed an extraordinary skill in sensing the potential of rough material. He has perfected his techniques and dexterity to render even the smallest of anatomical details on each of his carvings. He tries wherever possible to render accurately the colours, dimensions and proportions of his various subjects. When a single piece of rough material will provide a good combination of colours, he utilizes each of these to highlight different areas in his carvings. A good example of this technique is furnished by his renditions of monkeys in two-coloured obsidian. He carves the faces, hands and feet in one colour and the body in another.

Single pieces of gem material cannot be effectively used in such creatures as mallard ducks, kingfishers and peacocks, as all of these display such an extraordinary range of colours. It is with enormous skill that each part of the animal is carved in an assortment of gem materials. These are then assembled in a masterly way, so that they appear to be made from one stone.

Gerd Dreher has experimented with a wide range of techniques and styles, and in the last decade he has carved many animals with intricately carved bases. He has developed skilful techniques of cameo and intaglio cutting to produce the desired effects, and spends many hours carefully studying the numerous expressions of the creatures he carves, and he takes extraordinary care in making the animals' eyes. These are reproduced in a variety of ways, simulating as accurately as possible their colour, lustre, and form.

He studies all the latest equipment and tools, not only those made for carvers, but also those used by doctors and dentists, although much of his work is produced by using ancient and traditional techniques. His son Patrick was born in 1970 and has now joined him in the business. He is, in his turn, learning all the complex techniques of the lapidary art.

Gerd Dreher's talent is recognized today by a large number of collectors, and this enables him to be very selective in the materials and subjects he carves so that he need only undertake the projects he feels will yield the best results. His works are on public view in several parts of the world, and there are a number in private collections in Europe and the USA. All of his recent carvings are signed with his distinctive stylized monogram. There are permanent displays of his carvings at museums in Illinois and Pennsylvania, USA, in the principal museums of Idar-Oberstein, West Germany, and the National Museums of Canada. His work was specially featured at the Geological Museum in London during an exclusive exhibition specially prepared for the 50th Birthday of the Gemmological Association of Great Britain. There was a special exhibition of his work at the Los Angeles County Museum of Natural History in March 1991. (Gerd Dreher's carvings illustrated in this work are all in private collections.)

There are a number of very fine amateur carvers in various parts of the world. Many skilful amateur lapidaries have progressed to carving gem materials in cameo, intaglio and in the round. Examples of some of these items can be seen in a number of the local museums of Europe, the USA, and Australia.

The reader's attention is drawn to some modern techniques for reproducing cameos and intaglios. Large numbers of identical stone cameos are produced using hardened steel dies, which are engraved with the required design. These are then charged with diamond powder and ultrasonically vibrated to cut the basic cameo. In the better qualities finishing is done by hand, adding individual elements to the design. Intaglios are now copied by the use of a pantographic machine which will engrave the original design on to another stone. These techniques produce rather low-quality results, and on close examination all but the hand-finished products lack detail.

A CONCISE BIBLIOGRAPHY OF GEMSTONES

A considerable number of books have been written on gem materials over the last 2000 years. Some have been devoted solely to gems, others form part of major works on natural history in general. A considerable quantity of the information given in this work is taken from a wide selection of the books that are listed below.

There are a few books which are regarded as milestones in the history of gemmology. The Greek work by Theophrastus and the Roman natural history work by Pliny were the backbone of information relating to gem materials for over 1000 years.

In the medieval period there were many manuscripts written on the subject. Books by Marbodius, Agricola, and Steno were largely based on classical ideas, but they also incorporated many beliefs that were imported from the Arab world. These were brought into Europe in the thirteenth century and recorded in the manuscript "The Lapadario of Alphonso X, King of Spain".

The works of De Boot in the late sixteenth century were followed in 1659 by the first comprehensive book in English on the subject written by Thomas Nichols. The first recorded printed book on gem engraving and collecting in Latin was published in 1601 by Abraham Gorleaei. In 1750 David Jefferies published the first guide to diamonds and pearls. In 1813 John Mawe published the first really accurate guide to gems. In the late nineteenth century Harry Emanuel published a very popular work on diamonds and precious stones. A comprehensive survey of engraved gems was published in two works by the learned C.W. King. These were *Antique Gems and Rings* and *The Gnostics and their Remains*.

By the early twentieth century there were a number of reasonably accurate books written on this subject, among them Spencer's *Key to Precious Stones*, and the classic *Gemstones* by G.F. Herbert Smith, (which ran to sixteen editions). There are so many works (some on very specialized areas within gemmology) that have been published in the last fifty years, that the reader is advised to study the works listed in the bibliography, as these only give a general guide to a few of the many works now available on this subject.

Anderson, B.W., and Jobbins, E.A., *Gem Testing* (London: Butterworth, 10th edn., 1990).

Anderson, Frank J., *Riches of the Earth* (New York: Rutledge Press, 1981).

Arem, Joel E., *Gems and Jewelry* (New York: Bantam Books, 1975).

—— *Rocks and Minerals* (New York: Bantam Books, 1973).

—— *Man-Made Crystals* (Washington, DC: Smithsonian Institution Press, 1973).

—— Color Encyclopedia of Gemstones (New York: van Nostrand Reinhold, 1987).

Argenzio, Victor, *Diamonds Eternal* (New York: David McKay, 1974).

Bainbridge, Henry C., *Peter Carl Fabergé* (London: B.T. Batsford, 1949; repr. London: Hamlyn Publishing Group, 1966).

Bancroft, Peter, *Gem and Crystal Treasures* (Fallbrook, California: Western Enterprises-Mineralogical Record, 1984).

Bank, Hermann, *From The World of Gemstones* (Innsbruck: Penguin, 1973).

Battey, M.H., *Mineralogy for Students* (London, Longman: 2nd edn., 1981).

Bauer, Max, *Precious Stones* (New York: Charles Griffin & Co., 1904; repr. in 2 vols., New York: Dover Publications 1968).

Beck, Russell J., *New Zealand Jade: The Story of Greenstone* (Wellington: A.H. and A.W. Reed, 1970).

Becker, Vivienne, *Antique and 20th Century Jewellery* (London: N.A.G. Press, 1980).

Black, J. Anderson, *The Story of Jewelry* (New York: William Morrow, 1974).

Blakey, George G., *The Diamond* (London: Paddington Press, 1977).

Bloss, F. Donald, *An Introduction to the Methods of Crystallography* (New York: Holt, Rinehart and Winston, 1961).

Boardman, J., *Island Gems, A Study of Greek Seals in the Geometric and Early Archaic Periods* (London: Thames and Hudson, 1963).

—— "Archaic Finger Rings", *Antike Kunste*, x (London: Thames and Hudson, 1967).

—— *Engraved Gems, The Ionides Collection* (London: Thames and Hudson, 1968).

—— *Archaic Greek Gems, Schools and Artists in the Sixth and Early Fifth Century* (London: Thames and Hudson, 1968)

Bonner, C. *Studies in Magical Amulets* (University of Michigan Studies, Humanistic Series, xlix, 1950).

Bradford, Ernie, *Four Centuries of European Jewellery* (Country Life 1953, repr. Feltham: Spring Books, 1967).

Bruton, Eric, *Diamonds* (Philadelphia: Chilton, 2nd edn., 1978).

Buckley, H.E., *Crystal Growth* (New York: Wiley, 1951).

Chapman, Leo, *Diamonds in Australia* (Sydney: Bay Books, 1980).

Chase, G.H., "A Guide to the Classical Collection, Museum of Fine Arts, Boston" (1950, *passim*). 2nd edn., amplified by C. Vermeule.

Chu, Arthur, and Chu, Grace, *The Collectors Book of Jade* (New York: Crown, 1978).

Cipriani, C., and Borelli, A., *Simon and Schuster's Guide to Gems and Precious Stones* (New York: Simon and Schuster, 1986).

Copeland, Lawrence L., *Diamonds . . . Famous, Notable and Unique* (Los Angeles: Gemological Institute of America, 1974).

Dalton, O.M., "Catalogue of the Engraved Gems of the Post-Classical Periods" (London: British Museum, Dept. of British and Medieval Antiquities, 1915).

DeBeers Consolidated Mines, Ltd., *Notable Diamonds of the World* (New York: N.W. Ayer Public Relations, 1971).

Deer, W.A., Howie, R.A., and Zussman, J., *Rock Forming Minerals*, Vol. 1–5 (New York: Wiley, 1962–63).

Desautels, Paul E., *The Gem Kingdom* (New York: Random House, 1970).

Dickinson, Joan Y., *The Book of Diamonds* (New York: Crown, 1965).

—— *The Book of Pearls* (New York: Crown, 1968).

Dietrich, R.V., *The Tourmaline Group* (New York: Van Nostrand Reinhold, 1985).

Easby, Elizabeth K., *Pre-Columbian Jade from Costa Rica* (New York: Andre Emmerich, 1968).

Elwell, Dennis, *Man-Made Gemstones* (Chichester: Ellis Horwood; New York: Halstead Press, 1979).

Eppler, W.F., *Praktische Gemmologie* (Stuttgart: Ruhle-Diebener-Verlag KG, 1973).

Evans, Joan, *A History of Jewellery, 1100–1870* (Boston: Boston Book & Art, 1970).

Evans, R.C., *An Introduction to Crystal Chemistry* (Cambridge: Cambridge University Press, 2nd edn., 1964).

Faraday Society, *Crystal Growth* (London: Butterworth Scientific Publications, 1959).

Field, J., *The Properties of Diamond* (London: Academic Press, 1979).

Flower, Margaret, *Victorian Jewellery* (New York: A.S. Barnes, 1967).

Fossing, P., "Catalogue of the Antique Engraved Gems and Cameos" (Thorvaldsen Museum, 1929).

Freedman, Michael, *The Diamond Book* (Homewood, Ill.: Dow Jones-Irwin, 1980).

Fregnac, Claude, *Jewellery from the Renaissance to Art Nouveau* (London: Octopus Books, 1973).

Frondel, Clifford, *The System of Mineralogy*, Vol.3, *The Silica Minerals* (New York: Wiley, 1962).

Frye, Keith, *The Encyclopedia of Mineralogy* (Stroudsburg, Philadelphia: Hutchinson Ross, 1981).

Gaal, Robert A.P., *The Diamond Dictionary* (Santa Monica California: Gemological Institute of America, 2nd edn., 1977).

Gems and Gemology (Los Angeles, Gemological Institute of America; quarterly).

Gere, Charlotte, *Victorian Jewelry Design* (Chicago: Henry Regnery, 1972).

Gilman, J.J. (ed.), *The Art and Science of Growing Crystals* (New York: Wiley, 1963).

Greenbaum, Walter W., *The Gemstone Identifier* (New York: Arco Publishing, 1983).

Grigorietti, Guido, *Jewelry Through the Ages* (New York: American Heritage Press, 1969).

Grodzinski, Paul, *Diamond Technology*, 2nd edn. (London: N.A.G. Press, 1942, 1953).

Gubelin, Edward J., *Internal World of Gemstones* (Zurich: ABC Edition, 1974).

Gubelin E.J. and Koivula, J.I. *Photoatlas of Inclusions in Gemstones* (Zurich: ABC edn., 1989).

Guilhou Collection, Catalogue, Sotheby's Sale, 9–12 November, 1937.

Gump, Richard, *Jade: Stone of Heaven* (New York: Doubleday, 1962).

Hansford, S. Howard, *Jade* (New York: American Elsevier, 1969).

Hartman, Joan M., *Chinese Jade of Five Centuries* (Rutland, Vermont: Charles E. Tuttle, 1969).

Heiniger, Ernst A., and Heiniger, Jean, *The Great Book of Jewels* (Boston: New York Graphics Society, 1974).

Hey, Max, *An Index of Mineral Species and Varieties Arranged Chemically*, (London: Trustees of the British Museum, 1962, 2nd edn., with Appendix 1963).

Higgins, R. *Greek Jewellery* (London: Methven, 1961).

Holden, Alan, and Singer, Phyllis, *Crystals and Crystal Growing* (Garden City, New York: Anchor Books (Doubleday), 1960).

Hurlbut, Cornelius, *Dana's Manual of Mineralogy* (New York: Wiley, 18th edn., 1972).

Hurlbut, C.S., and Switzer, G.S., *Gemology* (New York: Wiley, 1979).

Journal of Gemmology (London Gemmological Association of Great Britain; quarterly).

Kalokerinos, Archie, *In Search of Opal* (Sydney: Ure Smith, 1967).

Knight, A.E., *The Collection of Camei and Intaglii at Alnwick Castle, Known as*

'The Beverley Gems' (1921, privately printed).

Koskoff, David E., *The Diamond World* (New York: Harper and Row, 1981).

Kraus, Edward H., and Slawson, Chester B., *Gems and Gem Materials* (New York: McGraw-Hill, 1939).

Kuntzsch, Ingrid, *A History of Jewels and Jewellery* (Leipzig: Edition Leipzig, 1979).

Kunz, George F., *Gems and Precious Stones of North America* (Scientific Publishing Co., 1892; repr. New York: Dover Publications, 1968).

—— *Curious Lore of Precious Stones* (1913).

—— *The Magic of Jewels and Charms* (1915).

—— and Charles H. Stevenson, *The Book of the Pearl* (New York: The Century Co., 1908).

Lapidary Journal (San Diego: monthly).

Laudise, Robert A., *The Growth of Single Crystals* (Englewood Cliffs, New Jersey: Prentice Hall, 1970).

Laufer, Berthold, *Jade – A Study in Chinese Archaeology and Religion*, Publ. 154, Anthropological Series Vol. X, Field Museum of Natural History, Chicago (repr. New York: Dover Publications, 1974).

Leechman, Frank, *The Opal Book* (Sydney: Ure Smith, 5th edn., 1973).

Lefever, Robert A., *Preparation and Properties of Solid Materials*, Vol. 1, *Aspects of Crystal Growth* (New York: Marcel Dekker, 1971).

Leiper, Hugh (ed.), *The Agates of North America* (San Diego: The Lapidary Journal, 1966).

Lenzen, Godehard, *The History of Diamond Production and the Diamond Trade* (New York: Praeger, 1966).

Liddicoat, Richard T., Jr., *Handbook of Gem Identification* (Los Angeles: Gemological Institute of America, 1972).

Mac Daniel, R.H., *Stamped and Inscribed Objects from Seleucus on the Tigris*, University of Michigan Studies, xxv (1935).

MacInnes, Daniel, *Synthetic Gem and*

Allied Crystal Manufacture (Park Ridge, New Jersey: Noyes Data Corp., 1973).

Maillard, Robert (ed.), *Diamonds: Myth, Magic and Reality* (New York: Crown, 1980).

Meen, V.B., and Tushingham, A.D., *Crown Jewels of Iran* (Toronto: University of Toronto Press, 1968).

Mercer, I., *Crystals. Full colour guide to natural crystals* (London: Natural History Museum and Harvard UP, 1990).

Mitchell, Richard S., *Mineral Names: What Do They Mean?* (New York: Van Nostrand Reinhold, 1979).

Myres, J.L., *Handbook of the Cesnola Collection of Antiquities from Cyprus* (New York: Metropolitan Museum of Art, 1914).

Nassau, Kurt, *Gems Made By Man* (Radnor, Philadelphia: Chilton, 1980).

—— *Gemstone Enhancement. The methods used in the treatment of treated stones* (London: Butterworth, 1984).

—— *The Physics and Chemistry of Colour* (Chichester: John Wiley and Sons, 1983).

O'Donoghue, Michael, *Synthetic Gem Materials* (London: Worshipful Company of Goldsmiths, 1979).

—— *A Guide to Man-Made Gemstones* (New York: Van Nostrand Reinhold, 1983).

O'Leary, Barrie, *A Field Guide to Australian Opals* (Australia: Rigby, 1977).

Oman, C., "Catalogue of Finger Rings", (London: Victoria and Albert Museum, 1930).

O'Neil, Paul, *Gemstones* (Alexandria, Virginia: Time-Life Books, 1983).

Orlov, Yu L., *The Minerology of the Diamond* (New York: Wiley-Interscience, 1977).

Osborne, D., *Engraved Gems, Signets, Talismans and Ornamental Intaglios, Ancient and Modern* (New York: Henry Holt & Co., 1912).

Pagel-Theisen, Verena, *Diamond Grading ABC* (West Germany: published by author, 7th edn., 1980).

Palache, C., Berman H., and Frondel, C., *The System of Minerology*, 2 vols. (New York: Wiley, 1944, 1951).

Palmer, J.P. *Jade* (London: Spring Books, 1967).

Parsons, Charles J., *Practical Gem Knowledge for the Amateur* (San Diego: Lapidary Journal, 1969).

Peiser, H. Steffen (ed.), *Crystal Growth* (Oxford: Pergamon Press, 1967).

Read, Peter G., *Dictionary of Gemmology* (London: Butterworth Scientific, 1982).

—— *Gemmological Instruments* (London: Newnes-Butterworth, 1978).

—— *Beginners Guide to Gemmology* (London: Newnes Technical Books, 1980).

Rice, Patty C., *Amber, the Golden Gem of the Ages* (New York: Van Nostrand Reinhold, 1980).

Richter, G.M.A., "Catalogue of Engraved Gems, Greek, Etruscan and Roman" (New York: Metropolitan Museum, 1st edn., 1920; 2nd edn. 1956).

—— *The Portraits of the Greeks* (Oxford: Phaidon, 1965).

—— *The Engraved Gems of the Greeks, Romans and Etruscans*. Part one: *Engraved Gems of the Greeks and the Etruscans* (Oxford: Phaidon, 1968).

Roberts, W.L., Rapp, G.R., and Weber, J., *Encyclopedia of Minerals* (New York: Van Nostrand Reinhold, 1974).

Rostovtzeff, M., *Seleucid Babylonia, Bullae and Seals of Clay with Greek Inscriptions* (Yale Classical Studies, iii, 1932).

Sauer, Jules R., *Brazil: Paradise of Gemstones* (published by author, 1982).

Schumann, Walter, *Gemstones of the World* (London: NAG Press, 1977).

Shipley, Robert, *Dictionary of Gems and Gemology* (Los Angeles: Gemological Institute of America, 1974).

Sinkankas, John, *Gemstones of North America* (Princeton: D. Van Nostrand, 1959).

—— *Gemstones of North America*, vol. 2 (New York: Van Nostrand Reinhold, 1976).

—— *Gem Cutting* (New York: Van Nostrand Reinhold, 1962).

—— *Van Nostrand's Standard Catalog of Gems* (Princeton; NJ: D. Van Nostrand, 1969).

—— *Gemstone and Mineral Data Book* (New York: Winchester Press, 1972).

—— *Emerald and Other Beryls* (Radnor, Philadelphia: Chilton, 1981).

Sitwell, H.D.W., *The Crown Jewels and Other Regalia in the Tower of London* (London: W.S. Crowell, 1953).

Smith, G.F. Herbert, *Gemstones*, 13th edn. (New York: Pitman, 1958).

Snowman, A. Kenneth, *Carl Fabergé: Goldsmith to the Imperial Court of Russia* (New York: Greenwich House, 1983, first published 1979).

Sutton, Antony C., *The Diamond Connection* (Los Angeles: JD Press, 1979).

Tolansky, S., *The History and Use of Diamond* (London: Methuen, 1962).

Van Landingham, S.L. (ed.), *Geology of World Gem Deposits* (New York: Van Nostrand Reinhold, 1985).

Vargas, Glenn, and Vargas, Martha, *Descriptions of Gem Materials* (Palm Desert, California: published by authors, 1972).

Vermeule, C., "Greek and Roman Gems, Recent Additions to the Collections", (Boston: Bulletin, Museum of Fine Arts, lxvi, 1966).

Watermeyer, Basil, *Diamond Cutting* (Cape Town: Purnell & Sons, 1980).

Webster, Robert, *Gems* (Hamden, Conn.: Archon Books, 3rd edn. 1975; Newnes-Butterworth & Co., 4th edn. 1983).

—— and Jobbins, E.A., *Gemmologists Compendium* (London: NAG Press, 1986).

Westinghouse Research Laboratories, *Crystals Perfect and Imperfect* (New York: Walker and Co., 1965).

Wilson, A.N., *Diamonds from Birth to Eternity* (Santa Monica, California: Gemological Institute of America, 1982).

Wood, Elizabeth, *Crystals and Light* (New York: Dover Publications, 2nd rev. edn., 1977).

Woodward, Christine, and Harding, R., *Gemstones* (London: Natural History Museum, 1988).

Yaverbaum, L.H. (ed.), *Synthetic Gem Production Techniques* (Park Ridge, NJ: Noyes Data Corp., 1980).

INDEX